EX LIBRIS

VINTAGE CLASSICS

EVERYTHING FLOWS

Vasily Grossman was born in 1905. In 1941 he became a correspondent for the Red Army newspaper, *Red Star*, reporting on the defence of Stalingrad, the fall of Berlin and the consequences of the Holocaust, work collected in *A Writer at War* and *The Road*. In 1960 Grossman completed his masterpiece *Life and Fate* and submitted it to an official literary journal. The KGB confiscated the novel and Grossman was told that there was no chance of it being published for another 200 years. Eventually, however, with the help of Andrey Sakharov, a copy of the manuscript was microfilmed and smuggled out to the west by a leading dissident writer, Vladimir Voinovich. Grossman began *Everything Flows* in 1955 and was still working on it during his last days in hospital in September 1964.

BY VASILY GROSSMAN,
TRANSLATED BY ROBERT AND ELIZABETH CHANDLER

Life and Fate

The Road: Short Fiction and Articles

BY VASILY GROSSMAN,
EDITED AND TRANSLATED BY
ANTONY BEEVOR AND LUBA VINOGRADOVA

A Writer at War:
Vasily Grossman with the Red Army 1941–1945

VASILY GROSSMAN

Everything Flows

TRANSLATED FROM THE RUSSIAN BY
Robert and Elizabeth Chandler,
with
Anna Aslanyan

VINTAGE BOOKS
London

Published by Vintage 2011

3 5 7 9 10 8 6 4 2

First published by the journal *Oktyabr* in Moscow in 1989
and in book form in the collection *Vse techet: pozdnyaya proza*
by Slovo, Moscow, 1994

First published in Great Britain by Harvill Secker in 2010

Vintage
Random House, 20 Vauxhall Bridge Road,
London SW1V 2SA

www.vintage-classics.info

Addresses for companies within The Random House Group
Limited can be found at: www.randomhouse.co.uk/offices.htm

The Random House Group Limited Reg. No. 954009

A CIP catalogue record for this book
is available from the British Library

ISBN 9780099519164

The Random House Group Limited supports The Forest Stewardship Council
(FSC®), the leading international forest certification organisation. Our books
carrying the FSC label are printed on FSC® certified paper. FSC is the only
forest certification scheme endorsed by the leading environmental
organisations, including Greenpeace. Our paper procurement policy can be
found at www.randomhouse.co.uk/environment

Typeset in Garamond by Palimpsest Book Production Limited,
Falkirk, Stirlingshire
Printed and bound by CPI Group (UK) Ltd, Croydon, CR0 4YY

Contents

The last photograph taken of Vasily Grossman, on a bench near his Moscow apartment, spring 1964 (© Fyodor Guber)

Introduction

Vasily Grossman has become recognised not only as one of
the great war novelists of all time but also as one of the first
and most important of witnesses to the Shoah. 'The Hell
of Treblinka' (published in *Znamya* in November 1944), one of
the first articles in any language about a Nazi death camp,
was used as evidence in the Nuremberg trials. And there may
be no more powerful lament for East European Jewry than
the chapter of *Life and Fate* that has become known as 'The
Last Letter' – the letter that Anna Semyonovna, a fictional
portrait of Grossman's mother, writes in the final days of her
life and manages to have smuggled out of the Jewish ghetto
of a town under Nazi occupation.

Few novelists have incorporated more history into their
novels than Grossman. *Everything Flows* is a quarter of the
length of *Life and Fate*, but its historical scope is in some
respects broader. The central story – about the struggle of a
fifty-year-old man, Ivan Grigoryevich, to find a place for
himself in post-Stalinist Russia after losing thirty years of his
life to the Gulag – is interrupted by chapters about Moscow
prisons in 1937, about the sufferings of women in the camps,
about Stalin's destruction of Soviet science in the late 1940s,
about the anti-Jewish campaign of the early 1950s, about
Lenin and Stalin and the roots of 'Russian slavery'. Many of
Grossman's thoughts – especially the suggestion that Stalin
was heir both to the Russian revolutionary tradition and to

that of the Russian secret police, and that his paranoia arose in part from the conflict between these two forces within his psyche – still seem startlingly bold. The novel even has room for a small playlet, a mock trial that follows Ivan's chance meeting with the informer responsible, long ago, for his being sent to the camps: the reader is asked to pronounce judgement on four informers, four different 'Judases'. The arguments Grossman puts into the mouths of both prosecution and defence are unexpected and lively; as members of the jury, we are constantly taken off guard, repeatedly forced to change our minds. The trial eventually falls apart, dissolved by the reflection that the living have, without exception, compromised themselves and that only the dead – who, of course, cannot speak – have the right to pass judgement.

Some of these digressions are introduced as Ivan's thoughts or writings. The most powerful chapter of all, an account of the 1932–3 Terror Famine that brought about the deaths of three to five million peasants in the Ukraine, is narrated by Ivan's landlady, Anna Sergeyevna, just after she has become his lover. Anna Sergeyevna was herself involved, as a minor Party official, in the implementation of the measures that caused this famine. Anna is an attractive figure and we cannot help but identify not only with the middle-aged Anna telling the story but also with the young Anna of the time of the famine; once again, Grossman denies the reader the luxury of unalloyed indignation. This chapter about the least-known act of genocide of the last century is subtle, complex and unbearably lucid. Only Dante, in his account of Ugolino and his sons starving to death in a locked tower, has written of death from hunger with equal power.

Almost every step of Grossman's career – even after his death – has been marked by long delays and tedious, protracted battles. Editors, publishers and politicians seem to have responded to the painful and intractable nature of Grossman's subject matter with an equal intractability of their own. *For a Just Cause*, the fine but more orthodox war novel to which *Life and Fate* is a sequel, was originally titled *Stalingrad*. This title was abandoned after Mikhail Sholokhov, by then the grand old man of Soviet letters, asked contemptuously, '*Whom* have you entrusted to write about Stalingrad?'; Sholokhov's implication, clearly understood by everyone, was that a mere Jew had no right to be writing about one of the most glorious chapters of Russian history – let alone to be writing about it with such truthfulness. From 1949 to 1952, Grossman and his editors struggled to meet the demands of the authorities. No fewer than twelve sets of author's proofs remain, and the editors of the literary journal *Novy mir* made three abortive attempts to print the novel before publishing a heavily cut version in 1952. A less cut version was published in 1954, and a full version in 1956. As for *Life and Fate* itself, the manuscript was confiscated by the KGB and Grossman was told by Mikhail Suslov, a prominent member of the Communist Party Central Committee, that there was no question of it being published for the next two hundred years. Even after the satirist Vladimir Voinovich had smuggled a microfilmed text to the West, it took him almost five years to find a publisher for the first Russian-language edition – mainly, it seems, because of anti-Semitism among Russian émigrés. Grossman's friends and admirers were bewildered and shocked. In 1961, after what he always referred to as the 'arrest' of *Life and Fate*, Grossman said it was as if he had been 'strangled in a dark corner'. Dismayed at being unable to find a publisher twenty years later, Voinovich said it was as if Grossman were being strangled a second time.

Even after the first publication of translations of *Life and Fate* in the mid-1980s, Grossman's reputation grew only slowly.

Grossman would have had little time for postmodernism, and it is perhaps not surprising that postmodernism had little time for him. It may have been easier during the decade following the collapse of the Berlin Wall to imagine that we can be free of the weight of history, to believe that we need only adopt different metaphors, different visions – and reality will be transformed. Today, however, as the ecological crisis deepens and the West is drawn into one seemingly insoluble conflict after another, it is harder to doubt the stubbornness of reality – and Grossman's realism seems more valuable than ever. Grossman is, on occasion, both witty and joyful, but he is seldom ludic; he is not given to flights of fancy and he is linguistically inventive only when plainer, more ordinary words are inadequate. If, however, one accepts Coleridge's definition of Imagination as 'the power to disimprison the soul of fact', then Grossman was endowed with an imagination of supreme power and – above all – steadiness.

It is hard to believe that a single man could possess the strength to write with such clarity about so many of the most terrible pages of twentieth-century history – the siege of Stalingrad, the Shoah, the Terror Famine. The source of such strength must remain a mystery, but Grossman himself certainly linked it to the memory of his dead mother, Yekaterina Savelyevna. He felt guilty that he had not done more to save her in 1941, that he had failed to persuade her to join him in Moscow and so escape the invading German armies. This admission of guilt, however, seems not to have weakened him but to have lent him clarity and determination. This is clear from the guardedly optimistic conclusion to the story of Viktor Shtrum (in many ways a self-portrait of Grossman) in *Life and Fate*. After betraying men he knows to be innocent, Shtrum expresses the hope that his dead mother will help him to act better another time; his last words in the novel are 'Well then, we'll see [. . .] Maybe I do have enough strength. Your strength, Mother . . .'

Grossman believed that his mother was, in some way, alive and present in the pages of *Life and Fate*. In a letter to her on the twentieth anniversary of her death, he wrote: 'I am you, dear Mama, and as long as I live, then you are alive also. When I die you will continue to live in this book, which I have dedicated to you and whose fate is closely tied to your fate.'* Grossman's mother is no less present in *Everything Flows*. Anna Sergeyevna first comes to Ivan's bed on hearing him call out for his mother in a nightmare. And her account of the famine is similar in tone to Anna Semyonovna's last letter from the ghetto; these two chapters are among Grossman's supreme achievements, and both are laments – for millions who died, for whole worlds that were destroyed. Both chapters are historically truthful; both chapters are written with the sensitivity of a supreme poet.

Everything Flows is an unfinished work; Grossman began it in 1955 and was still revising it during his last days in hospital in September 1964. It is unbalanced in its structure, and the burden of history it carries is so overwhelming that most novels would sink under its weight. Nevertheless, *Everything Flows* is a work of art; important though it is as a historical document, it is far more than a historical document. Even if the essays on Lenin and Stalin cause us to lose sight of Ivan Grigoryevich for most of the last quarter of the novel, and even if Ivan eventually becomes barely distinguishable from Grossman himself, Ivan's fate still moves us. And the novel's structure, however schematic, carries meaning; central to this structure is the idea that the telling of stories, of histories – the telling of my story and your story, of her story and

* Fyodor Guber, 'Pis'ma materi, pis'ma k materi' (*Nedelya*, no. 41, 10–16 October 1988).

his story – can be a gift. In the first chapters Ivan and his cousin, Nikolay, approach their long-awaited reunion with great hopes. Ivan hopes to be released from the burden of all that he has seen and suffered in the camps; Nikolay – a successful scientist – hopes to be released from the burden of the guilt he feels on account of all the compromises he has made in order to stay 'free'. Nikolay, however, feels threatened by Ivan's presence – and the breath of the camps he brings with him – and no real conversation, no true exchange of stories, takes place. Ivan leaves abruptly, lonelier and more burdened than ever.

In the second half of the novel, Ivan finds understanding and love; and the failed conversation between the two cousins is balanced by a true conversation between Ivan and his lover. Anna Sergeyevna's account of the Terror Famine – an act of genocide in which she was complicit – is a gift of love. She tells her story lucidly, with absolute trust, and with absolute truthfulness. She is not trying to escape her pain by inflicting it on Ivan, nor is Grossman trying to escape his own pain by inflicting it on the reader. Grossman is simply doing what he can to remember the lives and deaths of millions who have been too little remembered.

Ivan accepts this immense gift, and he does his best to reply in kind. Anna is taken away from him – by illness and, eventually, by death – but this does not bring an end to their conversation. Just as Grossman continued writing letters to his mother, so Ivan talks to Anna in his imagination and writes down for her – in a school exercise book that had once belonged to her nephew – his uncompromising thoughts about Lenin, Stalin and the Russian 'slave soul'. Ivan fully understands the importance of this unbroken conversation; in the penultimate chapter he says to Anna, some time after she has died, 'Do you know? At the very worst times I used to imagine being embraced by a woman. I used to imagine this embrace as something so wonderful that it would make me forget everything I had been through. It would be as if none of it had ever happened. But it turns out that it's you I have to talk to, that it's you I have to tell about the very worst time of all. You yourself, after all, talked all through that first night. Happiness, it turns out, will be to share with you the burden I can't share with anyone else – the burden I can share only with you.'

This exchange of gifts is not, of course, enough to save Anna's life, nor is it enough to restore the thirty years that Ivan has lost to the Gulag. It is, however, enough to validate Grossman's claim that freedom does not die, that it is the essence of our humanity. For all the pain gathered within it, *Everything Flows* is a gift, Grossman's last gift to the world. And one of the most precious understandings it embodies is that, if we can speak truthfully and trustingly, our histories can cease to be burdens. Any story, truly told and truly listened to, can become a gift.

Robert Chandler

The Khabarovsk express was due to arrive in Moscow by 9 a.m. A young man in pyjamas scratched his shaggy head and looked out of the window into the half-light of the autumn morning. He yawned, turned to the people standing in the corridor with their soap boxes and towels and said, 'Well, citizens, who's last in line?'

Last in the queue, he was told, was a plump woman who had gone away for a moment. She was behind a man with a twisted tube of toothpaste and a piece of soap plastered with bits of newspaper. He himself would be behind this woman.

'Why's there only one washroom open?' said the young man. 'We'll soon be arriving in the capital – and the conductors' only concern is the circulation of goods; they're just thinking about their private deals and the packages they've been asked to deliver. What do they care about their duties to the passengers?'

A few minutes later, a stout woman in a dressing gown appeared, and the young man said to her, 'Citizen, I'm next after you. But I've had enough of hanging about in the corridor – I'm going to go and sit down.'

Back in his compartment the young man opened an orange suitcase and began to admire his belongings.

One of his three fellow travellers was snoring; the back of his head was broad and bulbous. A second – pink-complexioned, young-looking, but bald – was going through the papers in his briefcase. The third, a thin old man, was sitting and looking out of the window, resting his head on his brown fists.

Addressing the pink-faced man, the young man with the suitcase said, 'Have you finished with my book? I need to pack it now.'

What he really wanted was for his travelling companion to admire his suitcase. In it were some viscose shirts, *A Brief Philosophical Dictionary*, a pair of swimming trunks and sunglasses with white frames. In one corner, covered by some local newspaper or other, lay some grey village-baked shortbreads.

The pink-faced man answered, 'Here you are – *Eugénie Grandet*. I realised I'd read it last year, when I was on holiday.'

'It's a powerful piece of writing, there's no denying it,' said the young man. And he packed the book away in his suitcase.

During the journey they had played cards. And while eating and drinking, they had discussed films, records, furniture, socialist agriculture, the merits of various Houses of Recreation in Sochi, and which football team had the better attack – Spartak or Dynamo.

The bald man with the pink face was an inspector for the All-Union Central Council of Trade Unions;* he worked in a provincial capital. The shaggy-haired young man was returning from a holiday he had spent in some village. He worked in Moscow as an economist for Gosplan, the State Planning Committee.

The man now snoring on the lower bunk was a Siberian construction superintendent. The two younger men disliked him because of his lack of culture; he swore, and he belched after eating. Learning that one of his fellow travellers worked in Gosplan, in the Economic Science Department, he had said, 'Political economy – now what exactly *is* all that? Tells you why collective farmers go to the city to buy bread from the workers, does it?'

Once he had got very drunk in the bar of a junction station where he had gone, as he put it, 'on a brief mission'. After this he had kept his fellow travellers awake for a long time, sounding off about one thing after another. 'You can't keep to the law in our line of work or you'll never get anything done at all. To fulfil the plan, you have to work the way life tells you to work. Yes, you have to meet life's demands: "You scratch my back, and I'll scratch yours." Once – under the Tsar – this was called private enterprise. The way *I* put it is "Let a man live – he *wants* to live!" Yes, I could teach you a thing or two about real economics! Once I had my steelworkers registered as nursery-school staff for a whole quarter – until our new budget came through. Yes, the law tries to stop life, but life makes its demands regardless. Fulfil the plan – and you get a pay rise and a bonus. But who knows? You might end up doing ten years in the camps instead. The law fights against life, and life fights against the law.'

The two younger men said nothing. But when the construction superintendent fell silent – or rather, when he began to snore loudly – they said what they thought of him.

'One needs to keep an eye on people like him. Behind that comradely mask . . .'

'A wheeler-dealer. A man without principles. Bad as a Yid.'

This man was a nobody, an uncouth nobody from the back of beyond. It was infuriating to sense that he held cultured people like them in contempt. 'I've got prisoners working on my construction site,' he had said once. 'Their name for people like you is "tossers". But when the time comes to decide who built Communism, no doubt it'll turn out to be you lot who did all the ploughing.'* And with that he had gone off to the next-door compartment to play cards.

As for the last passenger, it seemed that he seldom travelled in a carriage with reserved seats. Most of the time he just sat there, his palms on his knees, as if wanting to hide the darns on his trousers. The sleeves of his black sateen shirt ended somewhere between his elbows and his wrists, and the white buttons on the collar and the chest made it look like the shirt of a child. There is something absurd and touching about the combination of white, childish buttons and the grey temples and exhausted eyes of an old man.

When the construction superintendent said to him, in the voice of a man used to giving orders, 'Move out of the way, Grandad – I need the table for my tea!' the old man jumped to his feet like an obedient soldier and went out into the corridor.

Inside his plywood suitcase with its peeling paint lay a loaf of crumbling bread and some threadbare underwear. He smoked *makhorka** and, after rolling a cigarette, he would go to the space at the end of the carriage, so as not to upset the others with his horrible smoke.

Sometimes his fellow travellers would offer him a piece of sausage; once the construction superintendent presented him with a hard-boiled egg and a glass of vodka.

Even people half his age addressed him familiarly as *ty*, rather than politely as *vy*. And the superintendent kept saying that when they got to Moscow, 'Grandad' would pretend to be a bachelor and marry a young girl.

On one occasion the conversation turned to the subject of collective farms. The young economist began criticising 'village layabouts'. 'I've seen it now with my own eyes. In the morning they just hang about outside the farm office and scratch their arses. The collective-farm chairman and the brigade leaders have to sweat blood to get them out into the fields. And all they do is complain. They make out that under Stalin they didn't get paid at all and that they hardly get paid even now.'

The trade-union inspector, thoughtfully shuffling a pack of cards, agreed with him. 'And why should our dear friends be paid if they don't keep up with their grain deliveries? They need to be taught a lesson – like this!' And he shook his white fist in the air – the strong fist of a peasant, though it had clearly not seen manual labour for many years.

The construction superintendent stroked his stout chest with its rows of greasy ribbons – he had evidently been awarded many orders and medals.

'There was bread enough for us in the army, on the front line. We were fed by the Russian people. And no one had to teach them how to do it.'

'You're right there,' said the economist. 'What matters is that we're Russians. Yes, Russians – that's quite something.'

The inspector smiled and winked at his companion. It was as if he were pronouncing those well-known words: 'The Russian is the elder brother, the first among equals.'*

'That's what makes one mad,' pronounced the young economist. 'These peasants we're talking about are Russians – not some national minority or other! One of them started haranguing me: "Five years we lived on linden leaves ... Since 1947 we've been working without any pay ..." They just don't want to work – and that's all there is to it. They don't want to understand that everything now depends on the people.'

He looked round at the grey-haired old peasant listening to the conversation in silence and said, 'Don't be angry, Grandad. The State has begun to address your needs – now it's up to you. You must all fulfil your duty as labourers.'

'Their duty!' said the construction superintendent. 'They seem to want to eat every day – what do they know about duty and consciousness?'

This discussion – like most discussions, whether inside or outside a railway carriage – was never concluded. An air-force major with gleaming gold teeth looked into the compartment and said reproachfully to the three younger men, 'Well, comrades? How about getting down to some work?'

And off they had gone to their neighbours – to finish a game of cards.

But now the long journey was nearly over. The passengers were packing away their slippers and depositing remnants of food on the tables: pieces of stale bread, chicken bones that had been gnawed till they were blue, pallid sausage ends wrapped in layers of skin.

The sullen conductors had already collected all the crumpled sheets and pillowcases.

The little world of the railway carriage was about to disperse. Jokes, faces and laughter would all be forgotten – as would chance confidences and painful confessions.

Ever closer drew the vast city, the capital of the great State. Finished were the thoughts and anxieties of the journey. Forgotten were the tête-à-têtes at the end of the carriage with the woman from the compartment next door, while just outside the clouded windows the great Russian plain rolled past before you – and the water in the storage tanks sloshed heavily about behind your back.

The close-knit world of the railway carriage – a world that had come into being for only a few days and that was governed, on its straight or curved path through time and space, by the same laws as every other man-made world – was now melting away.

So great is the power of a great capital that it makes every heart miss a beat – even the carefree hearts of those who are travelling there to stay with friends, to roam around shops, to visit a zoo or a planetarium. Entering the force field generated by a world city, entering its taut, invisible network of living energy, everyone feels a moment of confusion and apprehension.

After nearly missing his place in the queue, the economist had been to the washroom. Still combing his hair, he had returned to his seat. Now he was scrutinising his fellow passengers.

The construction superintendent was sorting out his expenses sheets. A great deal of alcohol had been drunk during the last few days, and his fingers were trembling.

The trade-union inspector had already put on his jacket. Entering the force field of agitated human emotions, he had grown timid and silent; his supervisor, a grey-haired, bilious old witch, was sure to have a few things to say to him.

The train rushed past brick factories and little village houses built from logs, past tin-grey fields of cabbages, past station platforms where the night rain seemed to have created grey puddles of asphalt.

On the platforms stood sullen men and women from the Moscow suburbs, wearing plastic macs over their coats. Sagging beneath the grey rain clouds were high-voltage power lines. In the station sidings stood grey wagons, ominously labelled 'Slaughterhouse Station. Circuit Line'.

And the train thundered on with ever increasing speed, with a kind of malign joy. It was a speed that flattened space and time, that cleaved through them.

Resting his head on his hands, the old man was sitting at the table and looking out of the window. Many years ago, a young man with a tousled, uncombed head of hair had sat in the same way by the window of a third-class carriage. The people then travelling with him had disappeared. He had long forgotten their faces and words. Inside his grey head, however, things had come back to life that had seemed as if they could no longer be in existence at all.

The train had already entered the Moscow green belt. Its grey, tattered smoke clutched at the branches of fir trees and, forced down by the rushing currents of air, streamed over the fences of dachas. How well he knew the silhouettes of these austere northern firs; how strange it was to see them beside light blue fences, beside flower beds planted with dahlias, the peaked roofs of dachas and the coloured window-panes of their verandas.

And this man, who during three long decades had not once remembered that the world contains lilac bushes – and pansies, sandy garden paths, little carts with containers of fizzy water – this man gave a deep sigh, convinced now that life had gone on in his absence, that life had continued.

2

After reading the telegram, Nikolay Andreyevich regretted giving the postman a tip – he had evidently come to the wrong address. And then Nikolay Andreyevich remembered – and gasped. The telegram must be from his cousin Ivan.

'Masha! Masha!' he called.

His wife, Maria Pavlovna, took the telegram from him. 'Give me my glasses,' she said. 'You know I'm quite blind without them.' After she had read the telegram, she said, 'Well, there's not much chance of him getting a permit to live in Moscow.'

'Oh, for goodness' sake . . . Don't talk about residence permits at a time like this!' Nikolay Andreyevich wiped his hand across his brow and added, 'Just think – Vanya's* coming and all he'll find here is graves, nothing but graves.'

'This is going to be very awkward indeed with the Sokolovs,' Maria Pavlovna said pensively. 'I know we can give him his present some other way, but it's still all very unfortunate. It's an important occasion. He's going to be fifty.'

'Don't worry. I'll tell them the whole story.'

'And then the news that Ivan is back, and that he came here straight from the railway station, will spread from the birthday dinner to the whole of Moscow.'

Nikolay Andreyevich waved the telegram in her face. 'Don't you understand? Have you no idea at all how much Vanya means to me in my soul?'

He was angry with his wife. All the same petty thoughts, every one of them, had passed through his own mind before she had said so much as a word. This had happened many times before. What he saw in his wife were his own weaknesses, though he did not understand this; he was unable to grasp that it was his own failings, rather than his wife's, that made him so very indignant. But then, because of his love for himself, he was also quick to calm down; forgiving his wife, he forgave himself.

He too could not stop thinking about Sokolov's birthday party; his stupid thoughts just wouldn't leave him alone. The news of his cousin's arrival was shocking not only in itself but because it made the whole of his own life, in all its truth and untruth, appear before him; he felt ashamed that missing a celebration at the Sokolovs' – and the Sokolovs' welcoming decanter of vodka – was occasioning him so much regret.

He was ashamed of the shallowness of his thoughts; it had occurred to him, too, that he would have to get Ivan a residence permit – and that this would be hard work. He too had thought about how all Moscow would get to hear of Ivan's return, and that, one way or another, this was sure to affect his own chances of being elected to the Academy of Sciences . . .

And now his wife was tormenting him, continuing to say out loud everything that was on his mind, insisting on bringing into the light of day thoughts of his that were not really thoughts at all, thoughts that were really only something chance and imaginary.

'You're very strange,' he said to his wife. 'You make me wish I'd received this telegram when you were out.'

This was a hurtful thing to say, but she knew that Nikolay Andreyevich would immediately put his arms round her and say, 'Masha, Masha, we're going to celebrate this together. Who else is there for me to celebrate it with?'

And that is just what happened. But there was still an unpleasant, long-suffering look on her face. It meant, 'Your sweet talk doesn't give me the least joy, but I know how to be patient.'

But then their eyes met, and the love between them put right everything that was wrong.

For twenty-eight years they had lived together without ever being separated; it is hard to understand or explain the relationship of people who have lived together for almost a third of a century.

She was grey-haired now; she would walk across to the window and watch as he, her grey-haired husband, got into his car. And there had been a time when they used to eat in a canteen on Bronnaya Street.

'Kolya,' she said quietly, 'just think – Ivan never once saw our son. He was arrested before Valya was born. And now that he's back, Valya is already eight years in the grave.'

This thought astonished her.

3

As he waited for his cousin to arrive, Nikolay Andreyevich thought about his own life. He was preparing to tell his story, to make a confession to Ivan. He imagined showing Ivan his apartment. In the dining room they had a fine Turkmen rug. 'Look!' he would say to Ivan. 'Damned fine rug, isn't it?' Masha had good taste, and Ivan knew very well who her father had been. And in Petersburg in the old days people had understood how to live well.

How would he find a way to talk to Ivan? Whole decades had gone by. Life had gone by. No, life had not gone by – and that was what they must talk about . . . Life was only just beginning!

What a meeting it would be! Ivan was arriving in Moscow at an astonishing time. There had been so many changes since the death of Stalin. And they affected everyone. Both workers and peasants. There was bread in the shops now. And Ivan was back from the camp now. As were many others. And Nikolay Andreyevich had also reached an important turning point in his life.

Ever since his student years Nikolay Andreyevich had felt dogged by bad luck. This was all the harder to bear because he was certain he deserved better. He was well educated; he worked hard; he was considered a witty raconteur; women were always falling in love with him.

He was proud to be thought honourable, a man of principle.

At the same time, he was entirely free of pious hypocrisy. He enjoyed listening to a good story over a meal, and he had an excellent understanding of all the complexities of dry wines – even though he often preferred to get straight down to the vodka.

When people praised Nikolay Andreyevich, Maria Pavlovna looked at her husband with sparkling, angry eyes and said, 'Try living under one roof with him! Then you'd get to know the real Kolya: Kolya the despot, Kolya the psychopath, Kolya the greatest egotist the world has ever seen!'

Each knew every one of the other's failings and weaknesses, and sometimes this knowledge was more than they could bear. Sometimes it seemed it might be easier to live apart. But they were quite unable to live apart; if they had, they would have suffered terribly.

Maria Pavlovna had fallen in love with Nikolay Andreyevich when she was still a schoolgirl. And everything that thirty years ago had seemed astonishing and splendid – his voice, his big forehead, his big teeth, his smile – all of these things, with the passing of time, had become still dearer to her.

And he loved her too, but his love had changed. What had once been central in their relationship had faded into the background, and what had once seemed of lesser importance had become central.

Tall and dark-eyed, Maria Pavlovna had been a beauty. Her gestures and movements were still remarkably graceful and her eyes had not lost their youthful charm. But what had been a flaw in her looks when she was young – the way her large lower teeth stuck out when she smiled – had become more noticeable with the years.

His continued bad luck remained a source of deep pain to Nikolay Andreyevich. At student seminars it had been the talks hastily flung together by that drunkard Pyzhov or by the red-haired Radionov that had generated excitement – not his own meticulously prepared papers.

Nikolay Andreyevich had become a senior researcher at a famous scientific institute; he had published dozens of works; he had successfully completed his doctorate. But his wife – and his wife alone – knew what torments and humiliations he continued to experience.

At the cutting edge of his area of biology there were only a very few researchers. One was an academician, two were Nikolay Andreyevich's juniors, and one had not even completed his candidate's dissertation.* All four respected Nikolay Andreyevich's decency and valued him as someone to discuss their ideas with. They were friendly and well disposed towards him – but they simply, and quite sincerely, did not think of him as a scientist.

Nikolay Andreyevich was constantly aware of the aura of tension and excited admiration surrounding these men – especially the lame Mandelstam.

A London scientific journal had once described Mandelstam as 'a scientist who is brilliantly continuing the work of the founders of contemporary biology'. Had this been written about himself, Nikolay Andreyevich could have died of joy.

Mandelstam often behaved badly. Sometimes he was sullen and depressed; sometimes he spoke in a haughty and patronising tone. When he got drunk at a party, he would mimic other scientists, referring to them as mediocrities or even as frauds and rogues. Nikolay Andreyevich found this extremely irritating. Mandelstam, after all, was criticising friends, people whose hospitality he enjoyed: when Mandelstam was eating and drinking in someone else's home, he probably called Nikolay Andreyevich a mediocrity and a rogue.

Nikolay Andreyevich was equally irritated by Mandelstam's

wife – a stout woman who had once been beautiful and who now, it seemed, loved only two things: card games played for money, and the scientific glory of her lame husband.

And at the same time he felt drawn towards Mandelstam. 'Life is never easy,' he would say, 'for people as special as he is.'

But when Mandelstam gave him a condescending lecture, he would feel very upset indeed. He would come back home cursing and swearing, raging at that upstart Mandelstam.

Maria Pavlovna regarded her husband as brilliant. The more Nikolay Andreyevich told her about the indifference and condescension shown by various luminaries towards him and his work, the more fervent her faith in him grew. This faith and admiration were as necessary to him as vodka to an alcoholic. They both believed that some people are lucky and some unlucky, but that in other respects everyone is much the same. Mandelstam, for example, was blessed by especial luck – he was a kind of Lucky Benjamin of the biological sciences. As for Radionov, he had as many adoring fans as if he were a famous operatic tenor – not that he looked much like one, with his snub nose and his prominent high cheekbones. Even Isaac Khavkin seemed to be blessed with good fortune – in spite of the fact that he had never completed his candidate's degree and that, being suspected of the heresy of vitalism,* he had never, even at the most relaxed of times, been offered work at any research institute. Instead, although he was already grey-haired, he worked at a local bacteriological laboratory and went about in torn trousers. But there was no getting away from it – academicians went along to discuss their work with him, and the research he conducted in his pitiful little laboratory generated considerable interest and controversy.

When the campaign against the followers of Weissman, Virchow and Mendel began, Nikolay Andreyevich was troubled by the harshness of the punishments meted out to many of his colleagues. Both he and his wife were upset when Radionov refused to confess his errors. He was, of course, dismissed; Nikolay Andreyevich cursed his quixotic obstinacy and at the same time arranged for him to earn some money by translating English scientific texts in his own home.

Pyzhov was accused of 'servility towards the West' and sent off to work in an experimental laboratory near Orenburg. Nikolay Andreyevich wrote to him and sent him books; Maria Pavlovna organised a New Year parcel for his family.

Newspapers began printing articles consisting largely of denunciations: of careerists and petty crooks who had obtained degrees – even higher degrees – through fraud; of doctors guilty of criminal cruelty towards sick children and women in childbirth; of engineers who had built dachas for themselves and their relatives when they were supposed to be building schools and hospitals. Nearly everyone denounced in these articles was a Jew, and their names and patronymics were cited with unusual punctiliousness: Srul Nakhmanovich . . . Khaim Abramovich . . . Israel Mendelevich . . . A hostile review of a book by a Jewish writer with a Russian pseudonym would include, between brackets, the writer's original Jewish surname. Throughout the whole of the USSR it seemed that only Jews thieved and took bribes, only Jews were criminally indifferent towards the sufferings of the sick, and only Jews published vicious or badly written books.

Nikolay Andreyevich was aware that it was not only street sweepers and drunks on suburban trains who enjoyed these articles. He himself was appalled by them – and yet he felt annoyed with his Jewish friends who seemed to look on these scribblings as portents of the end of the world and who were always lamenting that talented young Jews were not being

16

accepted as graduate students, that they were being barred from university physics departments, that they were no longer being offered jobs in ministries or in heavy – or even light – industry, and that Jews graduating from institutes of higher education were all being sent to work in the most far-flung parts of the Soviet Union. And whenever staff reductions were being made anywhere, it was always the Jews who had to go.

All this, of course, was quite true, but the Jews all seemed to believe in the existence of some grand State plan that doomed them to hunger, impoverishment of every kind, and death. Nikolay Andreyevich, on the other hand, thought it was all just a matter of a hostile attitude towards Jews on the part of a certain proportion of Party and Soviet officials. He did not believe that special instructions with regard to Jews had been issued to personnel departments or the admissions committees of higher education institutes. Stalin was not himself anti-Semitic and, in all probability, knew nothing about any of this.

And in any case it was not only Jews who were having a hard time. Old Churkovsky, and Pyzhov, and Radionov had suffered too.

Mandelstam, who had been the head of the research division, was demoted to a post in the same department as Nikolay Andreyevich. Nevertheless, he was able to continue his work, and the fact that he had a doctorate entitled him to a good salary.

But then came an unsigned editorial in *Pravda* about the contempt for Russian theatre exhibited by Gurvich, Yuzovsky and other 'cosmopolitan' theatre critics. This marked the beginning of a vast campaign to unmask 'cosmopolitans' in all areas of art and science, and Mandelstam was declared an 'anti-patriot'. Bratova, a scientist then working on her doctorate, wrote an article for the institute's 'wall-newspaper' with the title 'Ivan, Who Has Forgotten His Relatives'. It began with the words, 'On returning from his travels to distant regions, Mark Samuilovich Mandelstam has thrown to the winds the principles of Russian Soviet Science . . .'

Nikolay Andreyevich went to visit Mandelstam at his home. Mandelstam was upset. He was moved, though, that Nikolay Andreyevich had come to see him, and his haughty wife no longer seemed so very haughty. The two men drank vodka together. Mandelstam roundly cursed Bratova, who was his own student. His head in his hands, he lamented how his students, his talented Jewish students, were all being driven out of science. 'What are they all going to do?' he asked. 'Sell haberdashery from stalls in bazaars?'

'Come on now, it's not as bad as all that,' said Nikolay Andreyevich. 'There'll be work enough for everyone,' he went on jokingly. 'For you, and for Khavkin, and even for Anechka Silberman the lab technician. There'll be bread for all of you – and with a bit of caviar too!'

'Heavens!' said Mandelstam. 'What's caviar got to do with it? We're talking about human dignity.'

But as for Khavkin, Nikolay Andreyevich had been mistaken. Things had taken a bad turn for him. Not long after the publication of the article about the Killer Doctors,* Khavkin had been arrested.

That report – about the monstrous crimes committed by Jewish doctors, and by Solomon Mikhoels, the Jewish actor – had shocked everyone. It was as if there were a dark cloud over Moscow, creeping into homes and schools, creeping into human hearts.

On page 4, under the heading 'Chronicle', there had been a statement to the effect that all the accused had confessed during the investigation. There could be no doubt; the doctors were criminals.

Nevertheless, this seemed unthinkable. It was hard to breathe;

it was hard to go about one's work in the knowledge that professors and academicians had become poisoners, that they had murdered Zhdanov and Shcherbakov.

When Nikolay Andreyevich thought about dear Dr Vovsi, and about the brilliant Solomon Mikhoels, the crime they were accused of seemed impossible, unthinkable.

But these people had confessed! And if they were innocent but had confessed anyway, that implied a different crime. It implied that they were the victims of a crime still more terrible than that of which they were accused.

Even to think about this was frightening. It took courage to doubt their guilt. If they were not guilty, it was the leaders of the socialist State who were the criminals. If the doctors were not guilty, then Stalin himself was a criminal.

Meanwhile, doctors he knew were now saying that it had become painfully difficult for them to carry on with their work in hospitals and polyclinics. The terrifying official announcements had made patients suspicious, and many people were refusing to be treated by Jewish doctors. The authorities were receiving countless complaints about intentional malpractice on the part of Jewish doctors. Jewish pharmacists were being suspected of trying to pass off poisons as medicines. Stories were being told in trams, in bazaars, in public institutions of all kinds, about how a number of Moscow pharmacies had been closed down because the pharmacists – Jews working as undercover American agents – were selling pills made of dried lice. There were stories about maternity hospitals where women in childbirth and newborn babies were being infected with syphilis, about dental surgeries where patients were injected with cancer of the tongue and of the jaw. There was talk of boxes of matches imbued with deadly poison. Some people began recalling suspicious circumstances surrounding the deaths of long-dead relatives; they wrote to the security organs, demanding the investigation and arrest of the Jewish doctors responsible. It was especially sad that these rumours were believed not only by street sweepers, not only by semi-literate and semi-alcoholic porters and drivers, but also by writers, engineers and university students, even by certain scholars and scientists with doctorates.

Nikolay Andreyevich found this atmosphere of suspicion unbearable. Anna Naumovna, the large-nosed laboratory technician, was coming into work every day looking pale, with mad, dilated eyes. One day she reported that a woman in her apartment, who worked in a pharmacy, had in a moment of forgetfulness given a patient the wrong medicine. On receiving a summons to explain herself, she had felt so appalled that she had committed suicide; her two children – a girl studying at a music college, and a boy who was still at school – were now orphans. Anna Naumovna had herself started making the journey to work on foot – because of the drunks in the trams who were always starting conversations with her about the Jewish doctors who had murdered Zhdanov and Shcherbakov.

Nikolay Andreyevich felt horrified and disgusted by the new Institute director, Ryskov. Ryskov kept saying that the time had come to purge Russian science of non-Russian names. On one occasion he declared, 'Our science will no longer be a Yid synagogue. If only you knew how I hate them!'

Nevertheless, Nikolay Andreyevich was unable to suppress a sense of involuntary joy when Ryskov said to him, 'The comrades in the Central Committee value your work, the work of a great Russian scientist.'

Mandelstam was no longer working at the Institute, but he had managed to find work as an adviser at a workplace training centre. Now and again Nikolay Andreyevich would tell his wife to ring him up and invite him over. He was glad that Mandelstam, who had become nervous and suspicious, kept postponing their meetings – which he himself was now finding more and more painful. At a time like this it was better to be among people who enjoyed life.

When Nikolay Andreyevich heard that Khavkin had been arrested, he glanced anxiously at the telephone and said to his wife in a whisper, 'I'm certain that Isaac is innocent. I've known him for thirty years.'

Maria Pavlovna suddenly embraced him and stroked his head. 'I'm proud of you,' she said. 'I know how much you put yourself out for Khavkin and Mandelstam – and only I know how much they've hurt you.'

But it was a difficult time. Nikolay Andreyevich had to speak at a public meeting; he had to say a few words about vigilance, and about the dangers of gullibility and complacency.

After the meeting Nikolay Andreyevich had a conversation with Professor Margolin who worked in the Physical Chemistry Department and who had also given an important speech. Margolin had demanded that the criminal doctors be sentenced to death, and he had read out the text of a congratulatory telegram to be sent to Lidia Timashuk, who had unmasked the Killer Doctors and who had just been awarded the Order of Lenin. This Margolin was an expert on Marxist philosophy; he was in charge of the lectures devoted to the study of the fourth chapter of Stalin's *Short Course*.*

'Yes, Samson Abramovich,' said Nikolay Andreyevich. 'These are difficult times. I'm finding it hard enough myself, but you must be finding it still harder.'

Margolin raised his fine eyebrows and, pushing forward his thin, pale lower lip, said, 'Excuse me. I don't quite understand what you mean.'

'Oh, I just, I just mean in a general sense,' said Nikolay

Andreyevich. 'Vovsi, Etinger, Kogan – who could have imagined it? I was once an inpatient of Vovsi's myself. The staff loved him, and the patients trusted him as if he were the Prophet himself.'

Margolin raised a thin shoulder, twitched a pale, bloodless nostril and said, 'Ah, I see. You think that it must be unpleasant for me, as a Jew, to say what I think of these monsters. On the contrary, I loathe Jewish nationalism more than anyone does. And if Jews with a leaning towards America become an obstacle on the road towards Communism, then I shall be merciless – even towards myself, even towards my own daughter.'

Nikolay Andreyevich realised that he should not have talked about how much Vovsi was loved by his gullible patients. If a man could say things like that about his own daughter, then it was best to speak to him in the language of official formulae.

And Nikolay Andreyevich said, 'Yes, of course. What ensures our enemy's doom is our own moral and political unity.'

Yes, it was indeed a difficult time – and Nikolay Andreyevich's only consolation was that his work was going well.

It was as if, for the first time, he had burst out of the narrow space of his guild and into domains of the real world that had always been closed to him. People were seeking him out, seeking his advice; they were grateful when he told them his views. Scientific journals that had usually ignored him began to take an interest in his articles. He even received a telephone call from the All-Union Society for Cultural Ties with Foreign Countries,* an institution that had never before contacted him. He was asked to send them the manuscript of a still-unfinished book so that they could consider the possibility of its publication in the People's Democracies.

Nikolay Andreyevich was deeply moved by the advent of his success. Maria Pavlovna took it more calmly. What had happened was inevitable; it was, she thought, simply impossible for it not to have happened.

Meanwhile, the number of changes in his life only increased. He still did not like the new people at the head of the Institute. Even though they were promoting him and his work, he was repelled by their coarseness, by their extraordinary self-assurance, by their readiness to call their opponents toadies, cosmopolitans, capitalist agents and hirelings of imperialism. Nevertheless, he was able to see in them what was most truly important: their boldness and strength.

And as for Mandelstam – Mandelstam was wrong to refer to these people as illiterate idiots, as 'dogmatic young stallions'. What he himself saw in them was not narrowness but passion and purpose – a clarity of purpose that was born of life and oriented towards life. That was why they hated abstract theoreticians, hair-splitting *talmudists*.

And although these new bosses sensed that Nikolay Andreyevich was not the same as them, that he was a man who thought and behaved very differently from them, they still thought well of him and had confidence in him: he was a Russian! He received a warm letter from Lysenko, who was very impressed by his manuscript and suggested that the two of them work together.

Nikolay Andreyevich had no time for the theories of the famous agronomist, but this letter nevertheless brought him great pleasure. And it was wrong to reject all of Lysenko's work out of hand. And the rumours about his dangerous readiness to resort to 'police methods', to denounce any scientists who disagreed with him – these rumours were probably exaggerated.

Ryskov had invited Nikolay Andreyevich to give a paper debunking the scientific work of the cosmopolitans who had been driven out of the biological sciences. Nikolay Andreyevich kept refusing, although he was aware how much this annoyed Ryskov. The director wanted the public to hear the wrathful voice of a Russian scientist who was not a Party member.

It was around this time that rumours began to circulate about the construction in eastern Siberia of a vast city of camp barracks. These barracks, evidently, were for the Jews. They were to be deported – just as the Kalmyks, the Crimean Tatars, the Bulgarians, the Greeks, the Balkhars, the Chechens and the Volga Germans had already been deported.

Nikolay Andreyevich understood that he had been wrong to promise Mandelstam bread and caviar.

He felt troubled and anxious. Every morning he looked through the papers to see if the trial of the Killer Doctors had begun yet. Like everyone else, he tried to guess whether or not it would be an open, public trial. He kept asking his wife, 'What do you think? Will they publish day-by-day reports, with transcripts of the prosecutor's speech and of cross-examinations, with closing statements by the accused? Or will there just be a communiqué giving us the verdict of a military tribunal?'

On one occasion Nikolay Andreyevich was told, in the strictest confidence, that the doctors would be executed in public on Red Square. After this a wave of pogroms would sweep through the entire country and – to protect them from the just but merciless rage of the people – the Jews would all be deported to Siberia and to Turkmenistan, to work on the construction of the Turkmen Canal through the Kara-Kum Desert.

And this mass deportation would be an expression of the eternally vital spirit of internationalism which, while understanding the wrath of the people, could not tolerate lynchings and mob law.

Like everything else that took place in the Soviet Union, this upsurge of spontaneous fury had been conceived and planned well in advance.

Elections to the Supreme Soviet were planned by Stalin in exactly the same way; information was collected, deputies were chosen – and from then on the spontaneous nomination of these deputies went ahead as planned, as did their election campaigns and eventual victory in national elections. Stormy protest meetings were also planned in exactly the same way – as were outbursts of popular fury and emotional expressions of brotherly friendship. And in the same way, several weeks before the May Day parades, officials gave their approval to the texts of journalists' reports from Red Square: 'At this moment I am watching the tanks race by . . .' It was in this way that the individual initiatives of Izotov, Stakhanov and Dusya Vinogradova were planned; it was in this way that millions of peasants chose to join the collective farms; it was in this way that legendary heroes of the Civil War were brought into the limelight or faded into the background; it was in this way that workers came to demand the issue of State loans or the abolition of days off work; it was in this way that the entire nation's love for its great Leader was organised; it was in this way that secret foreign agents, spies and saboteurs were chosen – and in this way, after long and complex interrogations, that accountants, engineers and lawyers who until recently had not for one moment suspected themselves of counter-revolutionary activity came to sign statements confessing to all kinds of acts of espionage and terrorism. This was how great writers beloved of the people were chosen; this was how editors chose the texts of moving appeals, addressed to young sons fighting on the front line, to be read into microphones by wooden-voiced mothers; this was how Ferapont Golovaty's sudden patriotic initiative was planned; this was how Party officials chose people to participate in free and open discussions if, for some reason, free and open discussions were called for; this was how the texts of their speeches were carefully coordinated in advance.

And then, all of a sudden, on 5 March 1953, Stalin died. This death was like an invasion; it was a sudden irruption into this grand system of mechanised enthusiasm, of carefully planned popular wrath, of popular love organised ahead of time by district Party committees.

Stalin's death was not part of any plan; he died without instructions from any higher authority. Stalin died without receiving personal instructions from Comrade Stalin himself. In the freedom and capriciousness of death there was something explosive, something hostile to the innermost essence of the Soviet State. Confusion seized minds and hearts.

Stalin had died! Some were overcome by grief. There were schools where teachers made their pupils kneel down; kneeling down themselves, and weeping uncontrollably, they then read aloud the government bulletin on the death of the Leader. Many people taking part in the official mourning assemblies in institutions and factories were overcome by hysteria; women cried and sobbed as if out of their minds; some people fainted. A great god, the idol of the twentieth century, had died, and women were weeping.

Others were overcome by joy. Villages that had been groaning beneath the iron weight of Stalin's hand breathed a sigh of relief.

And the many millions confined in the camps rejoiced.

. . . Columns of prisoners were marching to work in deep darkness. The barking of guard dogs drowned out their voices. And suddenly, as if the Northern Lights had flashed the words through their ranks: 'Stalin has died.' As they marched on under guard, tens of thousands of prisoners passed the news on in a whisper: 'He's croaked . . . he's croaked . . .' Repeated by thousands upon thousands of people, this whisper was like a wind. Over the polar lands it was still black night. But the ice in the Arctic Ocean had broken; you could now hear the roar of an ocean of voices.

Many working people, many scholars and scientists, felt both grief and the wish to dance with joy.

Their confusion had begun when they first heard on the radio the bulletin about Stalin's health: 'Cheyne-Stokes respiration . . . urine . . . pulse . . . blood pressure . . .' A godlike sovereign had suddenly turned out to possess weak and ageing flesh.

Stalin had died! In this death lay an element of sudden and truly spontaneous freedom that was infinitely alien to the nature of the Stalinist State.

The State was shaken, just as it had been shaken by the shock of the German invasion of 22 June 1941.

Millions of people wanted to see the deceased. All of Moscow, all of the surrounding provinces, was flooding towards the House of Unions, towards the Hall of Columns. Outside the city, lines of trucks stretched for miles and miles.

The roads were jammed as far south as Serpukhov – and then as far as Tula, more than a hundred miles from Moscow.

Millions of people were going on foot, all heading for the city centre. Streams of people, like black, brittle rivers, clashed against one another, were squashed and flattened against stone walls; they twisted and crushed cars; they tore iron gates off their hinges.

Thousands perished that day. The tragedy of Khodynka,* on Nicholas the Second's coronation day, paled into insignificance in comparison with the death day of the earthly Russian god, the pockmarked cobbler's son from the town of Gori.

People seemed to go to their death in a state of enchantment, in some kind of Christian or Buddhist mystical acceptance of doom. It was as if Stalin – the great shepherd – were gathering up the sheep that had not yet been gathered, posthumously excluding the least element of chance from his terrible general plan.

Stalin's comrades-in-arms read the horrifying bulletins from the Moscow police stations and morgues and looked at one another. Their deep confusion was also linked to a feeling entirely new to them; they no longer feared the inescapable fury of the great Stalin. The boss was dead.

A month later, on 5 April, Nikolay Andreyevich woke his wife with a wild cry, 'Masha! The doctors are innocent! Masha, they were tortured!'

The State had acknowledged its own terrible guilt. It had admitted that the imprisoned doctors had been subjected to 'impermissible means of interrogation'.

After the first moments of clarity and happiness, Nikolay Andreyevich unexpectedly began to experience a turbid, aching feeling that he had never known before.

It was a new, strange and very particular sense of guilt – guilt with regard to his own moral weakness, to his speech at the meeting, to his having signed the collective letter denouncing the monster doctors, and to his willingness to consent to an obvious lie. Guilt with regard to the genuineness and sincerity of his consent; it had come from the bottom of his heart.

Had he lived right? Was he really, as everyone around him appeared to think, an honest man?

This aching sense of repentance grew only stronger.

Now that the divinely impeccable State was repenting of its crimes, Nikolay Andreyevich began to sense that the State's body, the State's flesh, was in fact mortal and earthly. It too, like Stalin, suffered heart tremors; it too had albumen in its urine.

The divine impeccability of the immortal State turned out not only to have repressed individual human beings but also to have defended them, to have comforted them in their weakness, to have justified their insignificance. The State had taken on its iron shoulders the entire weight of responsibility; it had liberated people from the chimera of conscience.

And Nikolay Andreyevich felt as if he had been stripped, as if thousands of strange eyes were looking at his naked body.

The worst thing was that he too was there in the crowd, looking at his own naked body. Along with everyone else, he was studying his breasts, which hung down like an old woman's, his wrinkled stomach, which had been stretched by overeating, and the folds of fat on his flanks.

Yes, Stalin had had an irregular, filiform pulse; the State had excreted urine; and beneath his expensive suit Nikolay Andreyevich turned out to have been naked.

Examination of one's own self – how very unpleasant it was. The list of one's despicable acts was unbelievably odious.

It included general meetings of the Institute; sessions of the scientific council; solemn meetings on important anniversaries; routine briefings in the laboratory; little articles; two books; banquets; celebrations in the homes of the important and evil; voting in elections; jokes told during dinners; conversations with the directors of personnel departments; letters he had signed; an audience with the minister.

And the scroll of his life* contained all too many letters of another kind: letters unwritten – although it had been his sacred duty to write them. Silence – when it had been his sacred duty to speak; a telephone number it was imperative to ring, and that he had not rung; visits it was sinful not to pay, and that he had not paid; telegrams never sent; money never sent. Many, many things were missing from the scroll of his life.

And, now that he was naked, it was absurd to take pride in what he had always prided himself on: that he had never denounced anyone; that he had refused, when summoned

29

to the Lubyanka,* to provide compromising information about an arrested colleague; that, instead of turning away when he happened to meet the wife of an exiled colleague, he had shaken her hand and asked after the health of their children.

No, he did not have so very much to feel proud about . . .

His entire life had been a single act of obedience, with not one moment of refusing to obey.

And as for Ivan – Ivan had spent three decades in prisons and camps, and Nikolay Andreyevich, who had always felt proud about not having officially disowned Ivan, had not written him even a single letter. And when Nikolay Andreyevich had once received a letter from Ivan, he had asked his elderly aunt to reply.

What had once felt entirely natural had now begun to trouble him, to gnaw at him.

He remembered how in 1937, at a meeting called in connection with the Moscow Trials,* he had voted in favour of the death penalty for Rykov and Bukharin.

He had not thought about those meetings for seventeen years.

At the time he had found it strange, even crazy, that the poet Boris Pasternak and a Mining Institute professor whose name he had forgotten had refused to vote for the death penalty. The criminals had, after all, confessed during the trials. They had been questioned in public by a man with a university degree, Andrey Yanuaryevich Vyshinsky. There had been no doubt about their guilt, not a shadow of a doubt.

But now – now Nikolay Andreyevich remembered that there had been doubt; his certainty of Bukharin's guilt had been a pretence. Even if he had been certain, in his heart and soul, of Bukharin's complete innocence, he would still have voted for the death penalty – and so it had been easier for him not to doubt, to pretend to himself that he had no doubts. It was impossible for him not to vote for the death penalty; he believed, after all, in the ideals of the Party of Lenin and Stalin.

He believed, after all, that a socialist society, a society without private property, had been constructed for the first time in history and that socialism required the dictatorship of the State. To harbour the least doubt about Bukharin's guilt, to have refused to vote, would have meant that he had doubts about this mighty State and its great ideals.

And yet, somewhere in the depth of his soul, there had been doubt – even with regard to this sacred faith.

Could this really be socialism – with the labour camps of Kolyma, with the horrors of collectivisation, with the cannibalism and the millions of deaths during the famine? Yes, there were times when a very different understanding had found its way into the borderlands of his consciousness: that the Terror really had been very inhuman, that the sufferings of the workers and peasants had been very great indeed.

Yes, his whole life had passed by in obeisance, in a great act of submission, in fear of hunger, torture and forced labour in Siberia. But there had also been a particularly vile fear – the fear of receiving not black caviar but red caviar, mere salmon caviar, in his weekly parcel of food from the Institute.* And this vile, 'caviar' fear had co-opted his adolescent dreams from the time of War Communism;* it had made use of them for its own shameful ends. What mattered was to have no doubts or hesitations; what mattered was to cast his vote, to sign his name, without a second thought. Yes, yes, what had nourished his unshakeable ideals had been two very different fears: fear for his own skin – of being skinned alive – and fear of losing his entitlement to a bit of black caviar.

And suddenly the State had blinked. Under its breath it had muttered the truth – that the doctors had been tortured. And tomorrow the State would admit that Bukharin,

Zinoviev, Kamenev, Rykov and Pyatakov had been tortured, and that Maksim Gorky had not been killed by enemies of the people. And the day after tomorrow it would admit that the lives of millions of peasants had been destroyed for no reason.

And it would turn out that it was not, after all, the omnipotent and impeccable State that would be taking responsibility for the crimes committed. It was Nikolay Andreyevich who would have to answer for them – and *he* had had no doubts, *he* had voted for everything, *he* had signed everything. He had learned to pretend to himself so well, so skilfully that nobody, not even he himself, had noticed that he was pretending. He had, in all sincerity, prided himself on his faith and purity.

There were times when his self-contempt became so over-whelming that he began to feel bitterly, piercingly resentful towards the State itself: why, why had it confessed? It should have kept its mouth shut. It had no right to confess; everything should have been left as it was.

What must it be like now for Professor Margolin, who had said that he would be prepared, for the sake of the great internationalist cause, to put to death not only the Killer Doctors but even his own little Yid children?

Those many years of base submissiveness were too great a burden for his conscience to bear.

Gradually, however, this weight of depression began to lighten. Everything seemed to have changed and, at the same time, not to have changed at all.

The atmosphere of the Institute grew incomparably calmer and easier. This change became all the more tangible when Ryskov was dismissed from his post as director after irritating his superiors with his general rudeness.

And Nikolay Andreyevich finally achieved the success of which he had always dreamed; it was a true, important success – not just a matter of being recognised by officials and bureaucrats. It made itself felt in all kinds of ways: in journal articles; in remarks made by speakers at conferences; in the admiring looks of female colleagues and laboratory assistants; in the letters he now began to receive.

Nikolay Andreyevich was appointed to the Higher Academic Council.* Soon afterwards, the Presidium of the Academy of Sciences confirmed his appointment as the Institute's scientific director.

Nikolay Andreyevich wanted to bring back the 'idealists' and 'cosmopolitans' who had been expelled, but he found himself unable to get the better of the head of the personnel department – a woman who was charming and pretty, but terribly obstinate. All he could do was to provide them with piecework.

Looking at Mandelstam now, Nikolay Andreyevich wondered how this pitiful, helpless figure, coming in to deliver a package of abstracts and translations, could have been described only a few years ago, in the foreign press, as a very important – perhaps even great – scientist. Had he himself really longed so desperately for this man's approval?

In the past Mandelstam had dressed carelessly, but now he came to the Institute in his best suit.

Once Nikolay Andreyevich made a joke about this, and Mandelstam answered, 'An unemployed actor must always be well dressed.'

And now, as he recollected his past life, the thought of the impending meeting with Ivan filled him with a strange feeling, with a mixture of joy and bitterness.

The general view in his family had been that Vanya was the most talented and intelligent of his generation, and Nikolay Andreyevich had accepted this. Or rather, deep in his heart, he had not accepted this view at all; he had merely submitted to it.

Vanya had used to read through great volumes of maths and physics quickly and easily, not just absorbing what was written like an obedient schoolboy but understanding them in his own particular way. Even as a child he had shown a talent for sculpture; he had the ability to notice a facial expression, an unusual gesture, the essence of a particular movement – and to reproduce them in clay in a really quite lifelike manner. Most unusually of all, his interest in mathematics coexisted with a fascination for the ancient Near East. He had a good knowledge of what had been written about Parthian manuscripts and monuments.

His character, ever since childhood, had been made up of traits that could never, one might have thought, have been found in one and the same person.

During a fight at secondary school he – small as he was – had bloodied his opponent's head so badly that he had been held at the police station for two days. And at the same time he was timid, shy and sensitive. In a cellar he had set up a hospital for unfortunate animals – a dog that had lost one paw, a blind tomcat, a sad jackdaw with a torn-off wing.

As a student, Ivan had been an equally strange compound of, on the one hand, refined sensitivity, kindness and shyness and, on the other hand, a merciless sharpness that evoked resentment even in those closest to him.

It may have been because of these very traits that Ivan failed to fulfil people's hopes. His life had been broken, and it was he himself who had done most to break it.

During the 1920s many talented young people were denied higher education because of their social origin. The children of the nobility, of priests, of factory owners and of merchants were all barred from study.

But Ivan's parents were educated working class, and he was able to go to university. And he was not affected by the harsh purge of the socially alien.

And had he been beginning his life now, he would not have had any problems when he came to point 5 (nationality) of the countless questionnaires one had to fill in.

But had Ivan indeed been beginning his life now, he would, probably, once again have chosen the path of failure.

It was evidently not a matter of external circumstances. It was Ivan, Ivan alone, who was responsible for his misfortunes, for his bitter fate.

In a philosophy discussion group at the university he had had fierce arguments with the teacher of dialectical materialism. The arguments had continued until the discussion group was shut down.

Then Ivan had spoken out against dictatorship in one of the lecture halls. He had declared that freedom is as important a good as life itself, that any limitation of freedom mutilates a person as surely as an axe blow to a finger or an ear, and that the annihilation of freedom is the equivalent of murder. After this, he had been expelled from the university and exiled for three years to Kazakhstan, to the province of Semipalatinsk.

All that had happened around thirty years ago, and since then Ivan had probably not spent more than a year as a free man. Nikolay Andreyevich had last seen him in 1936, not long before his final arrest, after which he had been in the camps for nineteen years.

For a long time his childhood friends and student comrades had continued to remember him. 'By now, Ivan would have been a member of the Academy of Sciences,' they used to say. Or, 'Yes, there was no one like him, but then, of course, he was unlucky.' Some said, 'But all the same, he was mad.'

Anya Zamkovskaya, Ivan's love, had probably remembered him longer than anyone else.

But time had done its work and Anya, or rather, Anna Vladimirovna, by now grey-haired and in poor health, no longer asked after Ivan when Nikolay Andreyevich happened to meet her.

He had slipped away, out of people's minds, out of cold hearts and warm hearts alike. He existed in secret, finding it ever harder to appear in the memories of those who had known him.

Time worked unhurriedly, conscientiously. First the man was expelled from life, to reside instead in people's memories. Then he lost his right to residence in people's memories, sinking down into their subconscious minds and jumping out at someone only occasionally, like a jack-in-the-box, frightening them with the unexpectedness of his sudden, momentary appearances.

Time carried on with its extraordinarily simple work, and Ivan had already lifted one foot, about to leave the dark cellar of his friends' subconscious minds and take up permanent residence in non-being, in eternal oblivion.

But a new, post-Stalin time began, and fate decreed that Ivan should step back into the life that no longer gave him any thought and no longer knew what he looked like.

4

He did not arrive until evening.

There were many elements to their meeting. There was irritation because the lavish meal had been left sitting so long on the table; there was anxious excitement; there were exclamations about grey hair, about wrinkles, about all the years that had passed. And Nikolay Andreyevich's eyes grew moist, the way water rushes into a dry ravine after a storm, and Maria Pavlovna began to weep, once again experiencing the funeral of her son.

The dark, wrinkled face, the hessian jacket padded with cotton wool, the clumsy soldier's boots of the man from the camps – none of this fitted easily into a world of parquet floors and bookshelves, of pictures and chandeliers.

Suppressing his agitation, looking at his cousin through eyes dimmed by tears, Ivan Grigoryevich said, 'Nikolay, let me say first of all that I won't be asking anything of you. I won't be asking for money, or for help with getting a residence permit, or for anything else. And by the way, I've already been to the bathhouse, I won't be bringing lice or any other forms of life into your house.'

Wiping away tears of his own, Nikolay Andreyevich began to laugh. 'Grey-haired and wrinkled – but our Vanya, our dear, dear Vanya, is still the same as ever.'

He traced a circle in the air and then jabbed one finger through this imaginary circle.

'Unbearably direct, straight as a die, and at the same time – God knows how – kind and good!'

Maria Pavlovna looked at her husband. Only that morning she had been trying to convince him that Ivan Grigoryevich really ought to go the bathhouse to wash: a home bathtub just wasn't the same – and if Ivan did use their bath, they'd never be able to get the bath properly clean again, neither with acid, nor with lye.

There was matter of consequence in their inconsequential conversation. There were smiles, looks, hand movements, little coughs; all these helped to explain, to clarify, to reveal.

Nikolay Andreyevich wanted very much to talk about himself – more than he wanted to recall their childhood, or to list relatives who had died, or to question Ivan. But since he was well brought up – since he knew how to say and do things he did not want to say or do – he said, 'We ought to go and stay in a dacha somewhere, somewhere without telephones, and listen to you for a week, for a month, for two months.'

Ivan Grigoryevich imagined sitting in a dacha armchair, sipping wine and talking about people who had departed into eternal darkness. Many of their fates were piercingly sad; even the tenderest, quietest, kindest word about these people would have been like the touch of a rough, heavy hand on a heart that had been torn open. No, there were things that could not be spoken.

And, nodding his head, he said, 'Yes, yes, yes, Tales of a Thousand and One Arctic Nights.'

He was confused. Which was the real Kolya? The young man in the worn sateen shirt, with a book in English under his arm, who had always been bright, quick-witted and helpful? Or the man sitting opposite him – with the big soft cheeks and the waxen bald patch?

All his life Ivan had been strong. People had always turned

to him for explanations, for reassurance. Even the 'Indians'
– the criminals in the disciplinary barrack* – had sometimes
asked his advice. Once he had even broken up a knife fight
between the 'thieves' and the 'bitches'.* He had won the
respect of people from many different backgrounds: 'engineer-
saboteurs';* a ragged old man who had once been a Guards
officer in the Tsar's army; a lieutenant colonel, a real master
of the bow saw, who had served under Denikin in the Civil
War; a gynaecologist from Minsk who had been found guilty
of Jewish bourgeois nationalism; a Crimean Tatar whose
constant complaint was that his people had been driven from
the shores of a warm sea to the Siberian taiga; and a
collective-farm worker who had nicked a sack of potatoes
after calculating that, once he had served his time in the
camp, the document attesting to his release would entitle
him to a six-month city passport and so enable him to get
away once and for all from his collective farm.*

Today, however, Ivan Grigoryevich wanted someone else's
kind hands to lift from his shoulders the burden that he
himself was carrying. And he knew that there is only one
power in the world before which it is good and wonderful
to feel that you yourself are small and weak. But Ivan
Grigoryevich's mother had died long ago, and there was no
power that could release him from this burden.

As for Nikolay Andreyevich, he was now experiencing a
strange feeling that had arisen entirely involuntarily.

While he had been waiting for Ivan, he had thought with
intense feeling about how he would be supremely honest and
sincere with him, as he had never been with anyone in his
entire life. He had wanted to confess to Ivan all the sufferings of his conscience, to speak with humility of his own
vile and bitter weakness.

Let Vanya pass judgement on him. If he could, Vanya
would understand; if he could, he would forgive. And if

Vanya could not understand and forgive, well then, so be it. He had felt moved; tears had clouded his eyes as he repeated to himself Nekrasov's famous lines:

> *The son knelt down before the father;*
> *He washed the old man's feet.**

He had wanted to say to his cousin, 'Vanya, Vanechka, this sounds wild and crazy, but I envy you, I envy you because you did not have to sign vile letters in your terrible camp. You never voted for the execution of innocent men; you never made vile speeches . . .'

And suddenly, almost the moment he caught sight of Ivan, an entirely opposite feeling had appeared inside him. The man in the padded jacket, in soldier's boots, with a face eaten away by the cold and the *makhorka*-filled air of a crowded camp barrack – this man had seemed alien, unkind, hostile.

He had felt much the same during his trips abroad. It had seemed unthinkable to speak to well-groomed foreigners about his doubts; it had been impossible for him to share with them the bitterness of his sufferings.

He had spoken to foreigners not about his anxieties but only about what was central and indisputable – about the historic achievements of the Soviet State. He had defended his motherland – and himself – against them.

Could he ever have imagined that Ivan would evoke in him a similar feeling? Why? How? But this was indeed what had happened.

He felt now that Ivan had come here to strike a line through his whole life. Any moment now – and Ivan would humiliate him; he would talk down to him, he would treat him with condescension and arrogance.

And he desperately wanted to knock some sense into Ivan, to explain to him that everything had changed and begun anew, that all the old values had been erased, that Ivan himself had been vanquished and broken, that it was not by chance that Ivan's fate had turned out so bitter. Yes, yes, a grey-haired student – a loser . . . Who knows what he had been through? And what still lay ahead of him?

And it must have been because Nikolay Andreyevich so passionately and obstinately wanted to say these things to Ivan that he ended up saying exactly the opposite.

'Who'd have believed everything could turn out so well? As regards what really matters, Vanya, you and I are equals. And I want to say one thing to you: if ever you feel that you've lost whole decades and that your life has been wasted, if ever you feel this when you meet people who have spent their lives writing books and suchlike rather than felling trees and digging the earth – don't even give this feeling the time of day! In what really matters, Vanechka, you are the equal of all those who have moved science forward, the equal of all those who have succeeded in their life and work.'

And he felt his voice tremble with emotion and his heart ache with sweetness.

He saw Ivan's embarrassment; he saw tears of agitation once again cloud his wife's eyes.

He did, in truth, love Ivan. He loved him. He had loved him all of his life.

Listening to Nikolay Andreyevich trying to cheer up his unfortunate cousin, Maria Pavlovna felt that she had never before so fully sensed the strength of her husband's soul. Yes, she had no doubt who was the conqueror and who was the conquered.

It really was very strange. Not even when a ZIS limousine had taken Nikolay to Vnukovo airport – to fly to India and introduce a delegation of Soviet scholars to Prime Minister Nehru – not even then had she sensed so intensely the extent of her triumph in life. A very particular sense of triumph, mixed with tears for her dead son, and with pity and love for a man with grey hair and clumsy old boots.

'Vanya,' she said, 'I've prepared a whole wardrobe for you – you and Kolya are the same height.'

This was clearly not the moment to be talking about old suits, and Nikolay Andreyevich said, 'Heavens! Let's not talk about trifles like that. All that goes without saying, Vanya! With all my heart!'

'Your heart doesn't really come into it,' said Ivan Grigoryevich. 'What matters more is that you've got three times more flesh on you than I have.'

Maria Pavlovna was taken aback by the degree of attentiveness and perhaps even concern in Ivan's eyes. Her husband's especially modest manner seemed only to be making it harder for Ivan to renounce his old condescending attitudes.

Ivan Grigoryevich downed some vodka; his face flushed, turnng not so much pink as dark brown.

He asked after old friends.

It was decades since Nikolay Andreyevich had last seen most of his cousin's former friends; many were no longer alive. Everything that linked him to them – shared excitements, shared work – was now gone. Their ways had parted. His regret and sorrow for those who had disappeared forever 'without right of correspondence'* – even this regret and sorrow had now disappeared forever. Nikolay Andreyevich had no more wish to recall these people than one wishes to go up to a solitary, withered tree trunk with nothing around it but dead, dusty earth.

He wanted to speak about people whom Ivan Grigoryevich did not know – people linked to the important events of his own life. Talking about them, he would have been close to talking about what really mattered – close to talking about himself.

Yes, it was at moments like this that he needed to rid himself of that little worm, that sense of guilt that gnaws at every intellectual – that sense of the illegitimacy of all the wonderful things that had happened to him. What he wanted was not to repent but to assert.

And he began to talk of the people who had failed to value or understand him, who had benevolently despised him – and whom he was now doing everything within his power to help.

'Kolenka!' Maria Pavlovna interrupted suddenly. 'Tell him about Anya Zamkovskaya.'

Husband and wife at once felt Ivan Grigoryevich's excitement.

'She wrote to you, didn't she?' asked Nikolay Andreyevich.

'My last letter from her was eighteen years ago.'

'Yes, yes, she's married. Her husband's a physical chemist . . . his work has to do with . . . with those nuclear matters. They live in Leningrad – yes, in the same apartment where she used to live with her family. Usually we bump into her when we're on holiday, in the autumn . . . At first she always used to ask after you, but after the war, to be honest, she stopped.'

Ivan Grigoryevich coughed and said in a hoarse voice, 'I thought she must have died. She stopped writing.'

'Well, as I was saying about Mandelstam,' said Nikolay Andreyevich. 'Remember old Zaozersky? Mandelstam was his favourite student. Zaozersky was destroyed in 1937. The man had travelled abroad a lot; he'd associated freely with émigrés and defectors, with people like Ipatyev and Chichibabin . . . And as for Mandelstam, well, he got off to a brilliant start, but I've told you what happened to him in the end, how he was branded a cosmopolitan, and so on and so forth . . . All that, to be honest with you, is nonsense, of course – but thanks to Zaozersky he really was hand in glove with all his European and American scientific contacts.'

For a moment Nikolay Andreyevich genuinely believed that he was saying all this not for his own sake but for Ivan's sake. Ivan, after all, needed to be brought up to date: the values he lived by were childish and no longer relevant. And then he found himself thinking, 'God, how false I am! Falsity and hypocrisy have eaten deep into my soul.'

He looked at Ivan's brown, calm hands, and began to explain. 'You probably don't have a clear understanding of this new terminology: "cosmopolitanism", "bourgeois nationalism", "point five in the questionnaire". "Cosmopolitanism" means more or less what "participation in a monarchist plot" meant long ago, in the days of the First Congress of the Comintern. Although you must have come across all these people in the camps. The ones who took the place of those who had been removed – they too were removed. They too must have joined you there in the barracks. But I don't think we need worry about all that any longer – the process of substitution has been completed. And now there has been a majestic yet simple change in our lives: the national is no longer confined to the realm of form – during these last decades it has taken over the realm of content.* But many people are unable to understand this simplicity. After all, if you kick a man out of the house, he's hardly likely to see it as a consequence of the laws of history; all he sees is an absurd mistake. But the fact remains: our scientists and engineers have created Russian Soviet planes, Russian uranium reactors, Russian electronic computing machines – and our sovereignty in these realms has to be accompanied by political sovereignty. Russianness has entered the realm of content; it has become the basis, the foundation.'

He went on to say how much he hated the Black Hundreds,* the organisers of pogroms. And yet he could also

44

see that Mandelstam and Khavkin – who were undoubtedly gifted, capable people – had gone blind. To them, everything that was happening had seemed to be simply an expression of Judaeophobia – and nothing else. Similarly, people like Pyzhov and Radionov had been unable to grasp that what really mattered was not Lysenko's coarseness and intolerance; what mattered was the national, Russian science that he and his new men were affirming.

Ivan Grigoryevich's eyes were watching him attentively. Deep inside, Nikolay Andreyevich began to feel the kind of anxiety you feel as a child when you notice a sad look in your mother's eyes and you vaguely realise that you're doing or saying something wrong, something bad. Wanting to quieten this confused feeling, he adopted a tone of heartfelt eloquence. 'I've been through many tribulations,' he began. 'I've lived through a difficult, stern epoch. It goes without saying that I did not ring out loud and clear, like Herzen's Bell. I did not try to expose Beria, or the errors of Stalin. But it makes no sense even to try to imagine such things.'

Ivan Grigoryevich let his head droop – and it was impossible to tell whether he was dozing, daydreaming or pondering Nikolay Andreyevich's words. His hands were dozing; his head had sunk into his shoulders. Yesterday, listening to his travelling companions, he had sat in exactly the same way in the train.

Nikolay Andreyevich went on. 'I had a hard time under Yagoda, and I had a hard time under Yezhov. But now that Beria and Abakumov and Ryumin and Merkulov and Kobulov are no longer, I'm well and truly back on my feet. The main thing is that I sleep peacefully – I no longer expect visitors in the night. And the same, of course, goes for others. And now, now one can't help thinking that those cruel times were not in vain. A new life has been born, and we can all do our best to participate in it.'

'Kolya, Kolya,' Ivan Grigoryevich said quietly.

This angered Maria Pavlovna, who had noticed the look of bleak compassion on their guest's face.

Turning to her husband – who had also noticed this look – she said, 'Why are you too timid to say that Mandelstam and Pyzhov are infatuated with their own selves? Why keep lamenting that life has put them in their place? It certainly has – and thank God!'

This reproach, of course, was really aimed at their guest. Worried that she might have spoken too sharply, she continued, 'I'll go and get the bed ready. Vanya's probably very tired – more than we realise.'

But Ivan Grigoryevich – already fully aware that this meeting, far from bringing him relief, was merely adding to his burden – asked his cousin in a sullen tone, 'And you? Did *you* sign the letter condemning the Killer Doctors? I heard about that letter in the camps – from those who learned that your "process of substitution" was not yet complete . . .'

'What a dear, sweet eccentric you are!' said Nikolay Andreyevich – and he faltered, and fell silent.

Deep inside him everything had gone cold with anguish, and at the same time he could feel that he had broken out in a sweat, that he had gone red, that his cheeks were burning.

But he didn't fall on his knees. He said, 'My friend, my dear friend, it's not only in the camps that people had hard lives. Our lives have been hard too.'

'I'm not judging you!' Ivan Grigoryevich said hurriedly. 'I'm not judging you – or anyone else. Heaven forbid! No, no . . . How could I? Anything but . . .'

'No, no, that's not what I mean,' said Nikolay Andreyevich. 'What I'm trying to say is how important it is, in the midst of dust and smoke, in the midst of terrible contradictions, not to be blind – how important it is to keep seeing, to keep seeing the vastness of the road. If you go blind, after all, you can go mad.'

Ivan Grigoryevich said apologetically, 'The trouble is, it seems, that I don't know what's what, that I mistake vision for blindness.'

'So where are we going to put Vanya?' asked Maria Pavlovna. 'Where's he going to be most comfortable?'

'No, no thank you,' said Ivan Grigoryevich. 'I won't be able to spend the night with you.'

'Why not? Where else are you going to go? Come on, Masha, we'll have to tie him down.'

'No,' said Ivan Grigoryevich.

Nikolay Andreyevich fell silent and frowned.

'Forgive me, I just can't, but it's not . . . it's something quite different.'

'Listen, Vanya . . .' said Nikolay Andreyevich, and then said nothing.

After Ivan Grigoryevich had left, Maria Pavlovna looked at the table, still covered with dishes, and at the chairs that had been pushed back from the table.

'We gave him a royal welcome,' she said. 'As good as we gave the President of the Academy of Sciences and his wife.'

Mean, stingy people, on occasion, outdo generous, expansive people in the scale of their generosity. Maria Pavlovna had indeed prepared a lavish meal.

Nikolay Andreyevich went up to the table. 'Yes,' he said, 'if a man's mad, then he stays mad forever.'

She placed her palms on his temples and, kissing him on the forehead, said, 'Don't let it upset you. You really mustn't, my incorrigible idealist!'

5

Ivan Grigoryevich awoke at dawn, lying on the boards of a 'hard-class' railway carriage.* He listened to the noise of the wheels. Then he half opened his eyes and stared out into the grey dawn light beyond the window.

During his twenty-nine years as a prisoner, he had dreamed several times of his childhood. Once he had dreamed of a small bay. The water was calm, the seabed was covered with pebbles, and some little crabs had hurried past, moving sideways and silently in their underwater way, and disappeared into the seaweed. He had walked slowly over the rounded stones, feeling the gentle touch of the seagrass on his feet, and then dozens of elongated drops of quicksilver – baby scad and mackerel – had spurted out of the water and scattered. The sun had lit up the green underwater meadows and the clumps of spruce – and this beloved little bay had seemed to be filled not with salty water but with salty light.

He had dreamed this dream in a goods wagon. That had been twenty-five years ago, but he still remembered the despair that had gripped him when he saw the grey wintry light and the grey faces of the other prisoners, when he heard the creak of boots in the snow outside, the resonant knocking of the guards' hammers as they checked the bottom of the carriage.

Sometimes he saw a house overlooking the sea, the branches of an old cherry tree bending over the roof, a well . . .

He had developed his memory to a painful degree of

precision, and he could remember the gleam of a thick magnolia leaf, the flat stone in the middle of the stream. He remembered the design of the tablecloth – and the quiet cool of rooms with white, limewashed walls. He remembered sitting on the couch with his legs drawn up and reading a book – on a hot summer day the oilcloth was pleasantly cool. Sometimes he tried to remember the face of his mother, and his heart would ache, and he would frown, and there would be tears in his tightly closed eyes – just as in childhood, when you try to look at the sun.

He could remember the mountains easily, and in full detail; it was as if he were leafing through a familiar book, one that falls open by itself at the right page.

Scrambling through brambles and twisted elms, slipping on the stony, cracked, yellowy-grey earth, he would make his way to the pass and, after looking back at the sea, enter the cool half-dark of the forest . . . With their stout branches, the powerful oaks effortlessly raised up to the very sky their hills of intricate foliage; all about a solemn silence reigned.

In the middle of the previous century, the coastal areas had been inhabited by Circassians.*

The old Greek, the father of Methodius the gardener, had as a boy seen Circassian gardens and orchards, Circassian villages full of people.

After the Russian conquest of this part of the Black Sea coast, the Circassians had disappeared and life in the coastal mountains had died out. Here and there among the oaks were hunched-up plums, pears and cherries, now growing wild again, but there were no longer any peaches or apricots – their brief span was over.

Here in the forest lay sullen, soot-blackened stones that were the remains of ruined hearths; in abandoned cemeteries stood dark headstones that had already half sunk into the ground.

Everything inanimate – stones, iron – was being swallowed by the earth, dissolving into it with the years, while green, vegetable life, in contrast, was bursting up from the earth. The boy found the silence around the cold hearths especially painful. And when he came back home, the smell of smoke from the kitchen, the barking of dogs and the cackling of hens somehow seemed all the sweeter.

Once he went up to his mother, who was sitting at the table with a book, and hugged her, pressing his head against her knees.

'Are you ill?' she asked.

'No, I'm well, I'm just so happy,' he muttered, kissing his mother's dress and her hands, and then he burst into tears.

He was quite unable to explain to his mother what it was that he felt. It was as if, there in the half-dark of the forest, someone were lamenting, searching for people who had vanished, looking behind trees, listening for the voices of Circassian shepherds or the crying of babies, sniffing the air, hoping to sense the smell of smoke, of hot flatbreads.

And so, when he returned from the forest to the beauty and charm of his own home, he felt not only joy but also shame . . .

His mother had seemed unable to make any sense at all of his explanations. She had replied, 'My poor silly boy, you'll find life a struggle if you're going to be so sensitive and easily wounded.'

During supper, his father exchanged looks with his mother and said, 'Vanya, you probably know that our own Sochi was once called "Post Dakhovsky" and that the villages up in the mountains once had names like "First Regiment" and "Second Regiment".

'Yes, I know,' said Ivan, and sniffed sullenly.

'They were the bases of Russian military units. And these troops did not only carry rifles – they also carried axes and spades. They cut roads through forests inhabited by cruel, wild mountain people.'

The father scratched his beard and added, 'Excuse these grand words – but they were cutting a road for Russia. That's how we've ended up here . . . I've helped set up schools, and Yakov Yakovlevich, among others, has planted orchards and vineyards, and still other people have built roads and hospitals. Progress demands sacrifices, and it's no use weeping over what's inevitable. You understand what I'm trying to say?'

'Yes,' said Ivan, 'but there were orchards here before us – and they've been left to go wild.'

'Yes, my boy,' said the father. 'When you chop down a forest, splinters fly. But we didn't, by the way, force the Circassians to leave. They chose to go to Turkey themselves. They could have stayed here and become a part of Russian culture. As it is, they've suffered great poverty in Turkey and many of them have died . . .'

In the camp, Ivan had remembered many things from his past. He had dreamed of his birthplace. He had heard familiar voices. Their old watchdog, with rheumy, red-rimmed eyes, had got up to meet him.

And he had awoken to the ocean-like roar of the taiga, to the rage of a winter blizzard.

And now he was free – and he was still waiting for something good, something from his youth, to come back to him.

That morning he had woken in the train to a sense of irredeemable loneliness. The evening with his cousin had filled him with bitterness, and Moscow had seemed crushing and deafening. The vast tall buildings, the heavy traffic, the traffic lights, the crowds walking along the pavements – everything had been strange and alien. The whole city had resembled a single great mechanism, schooled to freeze on the red light and to start moving again on the green . . . During the thousand years of her history Russia had seen many great things. During the Soviet period the country had seen global military victories, vast construction sites, whole new cities, dams across the Dnieper and the Volga, canals joining different seas. The country had seen mighty tractors and skyscrapers . . . There was only one thing Russia had not seen during this thousand years: freedom.

He had gone by trolleybus to the south-western part of the city. There, amid country mud, amid village ponds that had only partly dried up, huge eight- and ten-storey apartment blocks had appeared. Village huts, small sheds and vegetable patches were living out their last days, squeezed from all sides by this vast stone and asphalt offensive.

In the chaos, in the roar of five-ton trucks, could be glimpsed the future streets of a new Moscow. Ivan Grigoryevich had wandered through this city that was coming into being, where there were still no roadways and pavements, where people walked to their homes along paths that wound between heaps of rubble. Again and again he saw the same signs: 'MEAT' and 'HAIRDRESSER'. In the twilight the vertical 'MEAT' signs shone red; the horizontal 'HAIRDRESSER' signs were a piercing green.

These signs, which had appeared along with the first residents, seemed to reveal man's carnivorous essence.

Meat, meat, meat . . . Human beings devoured meat. They could not do without it. There were still no libraries, no theatres, no cinemas, no tailors. There were not even hospitals, pharmacies or schools, but at once, amid all the stone, a red light had begun to shine: 'MEAT', 'MEAT', 'MEAT'.

And immediately after this – the emerald of the 'HAIRDRESSER' signs. Man eats meat, and he grows fur.

Ivan Grigoryevich had gone to the station during the night and found that the last train for Leningrad left at two. He had bought a ticket and taken his things from the left-luggage office.

He had been surprised by his sense of peace on finding himself in a cold, empty carriage.

The train had passed through the outskirts of Moscow. Dark autumn copses and glades had slipped by. It was good to be escaping from the vastness of Moscow – from its stone and cars and electricity; it was a relief not to have to listen any longer to his cousin's story about how the rational progress of history had cleared the ground for his own success.

On the shiny bed board, as if on water, gleamed a torch.

'Grandad, have you got your ticket?' a conductress asked.

'Yes, I've already shown it.'

For many years he had imagined the hour of returning from the camps and meeting his cousin, the only person in the world who had known him as a child, who had known his mother and father. But his sense of calm and relief on getting into the night train was not really so very surprising.

The loneliness he felt when he awoke was so total that it seemed to him more than any creature on earth, any air-breathing creature, could survive.

He was on his way to the city where he had spent his student years, the city where his love still lived.

When she had stopped writing to him many years ago, he had mourned for her. He had not doubted that only death could have broken off their correspondence. But she was still living. She was alive . . .

6

Ivan Grigoryevich spent three days in Leningrad. He went twice to the university; he went to the Okhta district and to the Polytechnical Institute. He searched for the streets where his friends and acquaintances had lived. Some streets and buildings had been destroyed during the Siege.* Sometimes the streets and buildings were still there – but the boards in the main entrances bore no names he recognised.

There were times, as he walked through all these familiar places, when he felt calm and abstracted, still surrounded by prison faces and the sound of camp conversations; and there were other times when he would stand before a building he knew, on a crossroads he knew, and some memory from his youth would pierce him.

He visited the Hermitage – to find that it left him cold and bored. How could all those paintings have remained as beautiful as ever while he was being transformed into an old man, an old man from the camps? Why had they not changed? Why had the faces of the marvellous madonnas not aged? How come their eyes had not been blinded by tears? Maybe their immutability – their eternity – was not a strength but a weakness? Perhaps this was how art betrays the human beings that have engendered it?

There was one occasion when the power of a sudden memory felt especially poignant – though the incident he remembered seemed random and insignificant. Once he had helped an elderly woman with a limp, carrying her basket up to the third floor for her. Afterwards, running down the dark staircase, he had suddenly gasped with happiness: puddles instead of ice, March sun, spring! He went up to the building where Anya Zamkovskaya had lived. It had seemed unimaginable that he might look again at the high windows and the granite facing of the walls, at the marble steps shining white in the half-dark, at the metal grille around the lift. How many, many times he had remembered this building. He had walked Anya home in the evenings; he had stood outside and waited until the light went on in her room. She had said, 'Even if you fight in a war and come back blind, legless and armless, my love for you will make me happy.'

In a half-open window Ivan Grigoryevich could see flowers. He stood for a while by the main entrance, then went on his way. His heart had not missed a beat. While he was still behind the barbed wire of the camps, this woman he had thought dead had been closer to his heart than she was today, closer than when he was standing beneath her window.

He both recognised and did not recognise the city. Many things seemed unchanged, as if Ivan Grigoryevich had last seen them only a few hours ago. Many buildings and streets had been reborn – entirely rebuilt. And much had disappeared completely, with nothing to take its place.

But Ivan Grigoryevich did not understand that it was not only the city that had changed. He too had changed. His concerns had changed; his eyes now looked for other things.

What he saw now was not what he had seen before; it was as if he had moved from one storey of life to another. Now he saw flea markets, police stations, passport registration offices, cheap canteens, employment bureaus, job announcement boards, hospitals, rooms in railway stations where transit passengers could pass the night . . . As for what he had known before – theatre posters and concert halls, second-hand bookshops, sports stadiums and university lecture halls, libraries and exhibitions – that whole world had now disappeared; it had slipped away into some fourth dimension.

In the same way, for a chronic invalid, nothing exists in a city except pharmacies and hospitals, clinics and medical commissions pronouncing on categories of disability. For a drunk, a city is built from half-litre bottles of vodka to be shared with two chance companions.* And for someone in love, a city consists of benches on boulevards, of two-kopek pieces for public telephones, of the hands of city clocks pointing towards the time of a rendezvous.

Once these streets had been full of familiar faces; in the evenings he had seen lights in the windows of his friends' rooms. But the familiar eyes smiling at him now were those of other prisoners, smiling at him from the bed boards of camp barracks. It was their pale lips that were whispering, 'Hello there, Ivan Grigoryevich!'

Here in this city he had once known the faces of assist-ants in bookshops and food stores, the faces of men selling newspapers from kiosks, the faces of women selling cigar-ettes. And in the camp at Vorkuta, a supervisor had once come up to him and said, 'I know you – you were in the transit camp at Omsk!'

But today there was no one he recognised among these vast crowds, nor did he strike up any new acquaintances.

People's faces had changed a great deal. Visible and invis-ible ties had been broken – broken by time, by the mass deportations after the assassination of Kirov, by the snows and dust of Kazakhstan, by the devastating years of the Siege. Ivan Grigoryevich was alone; he was a stranger.

Millions of people had moved and been moved. The streets of Leningrad were now filled by blue-eyed, high-cheekboned people from the nearby towns and villages – and in the camps Ivan Grigoryevich had met all too many melancholy figures whose inability to pronounce the letter 'r' revealed them to be natives of the old St Petersburg.

The Nevsky Prospekt and the backwoods had moved towards each other. They had mingled not only in buses and apartments but also on the pages of books and journals, in the conference rooms of scientific institutes.

Whether he was at a sign saying 'Passport Section', peering through the windows of a Leningrad police station or listening to his cousin hold forth as they sat at a lavishly spread table – wherever he was, Ivan Grigoryevich had sensed the spirit of the camp. Barbed wire, it seemed, was no longer necessary; life outside the barbed wire had become, in its essence, no different from that of the barracks.

Wreathed in flame, smoke and steam, a huge cauldron was bubbling, groaning and gurgling – and there were many people who imagined that they alone understood what was going on in its chaos. Many imagined that they alone knew how the stew had been cooked and who would be eating it.

In his soldier's boots, Ivan Grigoryevich was once again standing before the divinely barefoot, laurel-crowned horseman.* He used to pass this way thirty years ago; then too the bronze Tsar had been full of might. In Peter the Great he had, at last, met a familiar figure.

Never, neither thirty years ago nor a hundred and thirty years ago, when Pushkin had brought his humble protagonist to this square, had the wondrous Tsar seemed as great as he did today. No power in the world was vaster than the power he had gathered to himself and to which he had given expression – the majestic power of a wondrous State. This power had grown and grown. It now reigned over fields and factories, over the writing desks of poets and scholars, over sites where new canals and dams were being built, over quarries, sawmills and timber forests; in its great might, it was able to control both the vastness of space and the secret depths of the hearts of enchanted human beings who willingly offered up to it the gift of their freedom, even of their wish for freedom.

'*Sankt Peterburg, sanpropusknik, Sankt Peterburg, sanpropusknik,*' Ivan Grigoryevich began repeating to himself. This foolish jingle, linking the old capital's old name with the camp reception barracks where newly arrived prisoners were strip-searched, shaved, washed, disinfected and deloused, seemed somehow to express a link, a bond between the great horseman and the camp vagabond.

Ivan Grigoryevich spent his nights at the railway station, in the room for passengers in transit. He was spending only one and a half or two roubles a day, and he was in no hurry to leave Leningrad.

On the third day he bumped into someone he knew, someone he had remembered many times during his years in the camps.

They recognised each other straight away – even though Ivan Grigoryevich now bore no resemblance to the third-year student he had once been, even though Vitaly Antonovich Pinegin, now wearing a grey raincoat and a felt hat, also looked very different from the young man of thirty years ago who had gone about in a worn student jacket.

Seeing the stunned look on Pinegin's face, Ivan Grigoryevich said, 'What is it? Did you think I was dead?'

Pinegin spread his hands in bewilderment. 'Well, someone did tell me ten years ago that you had, you know . . .'

His alert, intelligent eyes were looking deep into the eyes of Ivan Grigoryevich.

'Don't worry,' said Ivan Grigoryevich. 'I'm not a ghost, nor, which would be far more unpleasant, am I a fugitive. Like you, I have a passport and everything else.'*

This made Pinegin indignant. 'When I meet an old comrade,' he said, 'it's not his passport that interests me.'

Pinegin had risen a long way in the world but he was still a good fellow, not someone to stand on ceremony.

Not for a moment, whether he was talking about his sons, or whether he was saying, 'You've changed a great deal, but I recognised you at once,' did Pinegin take his eyes off Ivan Grigoryevich; his eyes were greedy, fascinated.

'So then,' said Pinegin. 'There you are. What else should I tell you about?'

'*What you should really tell me . . .*' For a moment, Pinegin froze – but no, Ivan Grigoryevich had not really said anything of the kind.

'But you haven't told me anything about yourself,' said Pinegin. Once again he waited. Would Ivan Grigoryevich say, '*I don't need to – you know more than enough already. Yes, you had more than enough to say about me when there were people wanting to know*'?

But Ivan Grigoryevich said nothing. He just shrugged his shoulders.

And Pinegin suddenly realised: Vanya knew nothing, and it was impossible for him to know anything. It was all just nerves, his poor nerves . . . Why hadn't he chosen some other day to send his car in for a service? He'd been thinking about Ivan not long ago. One of his relatives, he had thought, might get him posthumously rehabilitated. Ivan would be transferred from the category of dead souls to that of living souls. And now here the man was, in broad daylight – Ivan, Vanya, Vanechka! He had done thirty years in the camps, and in his pocket, probably, was a document bearing the words 'Due to lack of evidence'.

He looked again into Ivan Grigoryevich's eyes and understood, once and for all, that Ivan knew nothing. He began to feel ashamed of his heart tremors, of his cold sweat, of how close he'd been to gibbering out something stupid.

And his certainty that Ivan would not spit in his face, would not hold him to account – this new certainty filled Pinegin with light. With a kind of gratitude that even he himself could barely understand, he said to Ivan, 'Listen, Ivan. Let's just be straightforward, like true workers. My old man, after all, was a blacksmith. Maybe you need money? Please, believe me, as a friend, with all my heart.'

Without a word of reproach, Ivan Grigoryevich looked with alert, sad curiosity into Pinegin's eyes. And just for one second – but not for two – Pinegin felt that he could sacrifice everything. He could sacrifice his decorations and honours, his dacha, his position of power and authority, his beautiful wife, his brilliant sons now studying nuclear physics – anything not to have to endure the look of those eyes.

'Well, Pinegin, all the best!' said Ivan. And he walked off towards the railway station.

7

Who is guilty? Who will be held responsible?

This question needs thought. We must not answer too quickly.

Here they all are: lying expert reports from engineers and literary critics; speeches denouncing enemies of the people; intimate conversations and confessions made to a friend – transformed into the reports and denunciations of informers and stoolies.

These denunciations were the prelude to an arrest; they were at hand throughout the investigation; they largely determined the verdict. These megatons of denunciatory falsehood served, it seems, to establish the lists of who was to be classified as a kulak,* who was to be deprived of their passport and the right to vote, who was to be deported, who was to be shot.

At one end of the chain were two people at a table, drinking cups of tea and chatting. Next, in cosy lamplight, someone cultured and educated composed a report; or perhaps an activist gave a frank and straightforward speech at a meeting of the collective farm. And at the other end of the chain were crazed eyes; damaged kidneys; a skull pierced by a bullet; gangrenous, pus-oozing toes gnawed by the frost of the taiga; scurvy-ridden corpses in a log hut that served as the camp morgue.

In the beginning was the word . . . That is truly so.

So what is to be done with these informer-murderers?

Here is one who has been released after twelve years in the camps. He has shaking hands and the sunken eyes of a martyr. We will call him Judas I. It has been rumoured that, long ago, he behaved badly under interrogation. Some of his friends refuse to greet him if they pass him on the street. Those who are a little more intelligent are polite to him when they meet, but they do not invite him back home. Those who are still more intelligent – and more generous and understanding – invite him into their homes but are careful not to let him into their hearts.

All of these friends have dachas, savings accounts, medals and decorations, cars. He, of course, is thin, and they are plump – but they did nothing bad under interrogation. Or rather, they were not in a position to do anything bad – they were not interrogated. They were lucky; they were never arrested. In what way are these plump men morally superior to this thin man? He too could have been plump; they too could have been thin. Was their fate determined by some law, or by chance?

He was someone quite ordinary. He drank tea, ate fried eggs, visited the Moscow Art Theatre, liked to talk to his friends about books he had read. Sometimes he was kind and generous. He was, admittedly, nervous, high-strung; he had no self-confidence.

And they put the heat on him. They did not merely shout at him; they beat him; they made him eat salted herrings while giving him nothing to drink; and they threatened him with execution. But still, what he did was a terrible thing: he slandered an innocent man. Admittedly, the man he slandered was never arrested – while he himself, forced into being a slanderer, did twelve years of forced labour and came back barely alive, a broken man, a pauper, on his last legs. But the fact remains: he committed slander.

Let us not judge hastily. Let us give serious thought to this case.

And now, here is Judas II. This man never spent so much as a day in prison. He had a reputation for being clever and eloquent – and then people came back from the camps, more dead than alive, and said that he had been a regular informer for the security organs. He had helped to destroy many people. For many years he had conducted heart-to-heart conversations with his friends and then handed in written reports to the authorities. His testimonies were not extorted from him by torture; on the contrary, he took the initiative, deftly and inventively leading his friends to speak about dangerous matters. Two of the men he slandered never returned from the camps; one was sentenced by a military tribunal and shot. The survivors returned with lists of illnesses each of which on its own – even by the Commission's demanding standards – would entitle a man to full invalidity benefit for the rest of his life.

In the meantime he had acquired a paunch – and a reputation as a gourmet and a connoisseur of Georgian wines. And he understood about culture: he was a collector, among other things, of rare editions of old poetry.

But let us not hurry. Let us think before we pronounce judgement.

Ever since childhood he had been frightened out of his mind. In 1919 his wealthy father had died of typhus, in a concentration camp. His aunt was married to a general, and the two of them had emigrated to Paris. His elder brother had fought for the Whites. He had lived in terror; terror had lived inside him. His mother had trembled when she spoke to a policeman, when she spoke to the building manager – or to the senior tenant in their communal apartment, or to officials from the city soviet. Every hour of every day he and his family had sensed their class inferiority,

63

their class depravity. At school he had trembled before the secretary of the Party cell; sweet, pretty Galya, the leader of the school Young Pioneers, had always seemed to look on him with revulsion, as if he were an untouchable, a worm. He was terrified that she might notice the adoring look in his eyes.

And at this point one begins to understand. This man had been hypnotised, enchanted by the might of the new world. He was like a little bird, unable to look away, captivated by the dazzling gaze of something new, brilliant and all-embracing. He so much wanted to become a part of it all, to be favoured. And the new world had taken him in. The poor little sparrow had not so much as let out a cheep, had not so much as fluttered his wings when the dread new world had said it needed his mind and his charm. He had offered his all on the altar of the Fatherland.

All this, of course, is true. Nevertheless – what a bastard! While he was denouncing others, he did not forget to look out for himself. He ate delicacies; he basked in the sun. And yet . . . he was terribly defenceless – the kind of man who really shouldn't be let out anywhere without a nanny, without a loving wife to look after him. How can a man like him be expected to resist a force that had conquered half the world, a force that had turned an entire empire inside out and upside down? This man, remember, was all trembling and delicate; he was like fine lace. You had only to touch him the wrong way – and he would seem lost and confused, his eyes full of misery.

And this deadly swamp viper had insinuated itself into the confidence of many people – and brought them great suffering.

And the people he destroyed were people like himself – kind, reserved, intelligent, timid people, his own oldest friends. He alone held the key to them; he was, after all, a man of real understanding, a man who had wept many times over Chekhov's story 'The Bishop'.

All the same, let's wait, let's think. Let's not condemn him without thinking.

And here is a new comrade: Judas III. He has a hoarse, clipped voice – the voice of a boatswain. His gaze is calm and searching. He has the assurance of one of life's masters. One moment he may be entrusted with ideological work, another moment with the management of agriculture. His answers on official forms, his answers to questions about his past and his social background, are impeccable, white as snow; they gleam with their own light. His relatives are all machine-tool operators or the poorest of poor peasants.

In 1937 he wrote more than two hundred denunciations at one go, without a second thought. The list of his victims is varied: commissars from the time of the Civil War; a poet and songwriter; the director of a foundry; two district Party committee secretaries; an old engineer (not a Party member); one newspaper editor and two publishing-house editors; the director of a special 'closed' canteen; a philosophy teacher; the director of a 'political enlightenment office'; a botany professor; a handyman employed by the superintendents of a block of apartments; two officials from a district agricultural administration office . . . It is impossible to list all of them.

All his denunciations were directed not against 'former' people but against people who were truly Soviet; his victims were Party members, men who had fought in the Civil War, activists. He specialised in the more fanatical Party members, gleefully slashing them in the face with his deadly, razor-sharp words.

Few of these two hundred returned. Some were sentenced and executed and shot; others put on 'wooden jackets' after dying of malnutrition or being shot in the course of camp purges. Some returned, physically and emotionally mutilated, to drag out their free existence as best they could.

For him 1937 was a time of victory. This sharp-eyed young lad had been poorly educated and everyone around him seemed superior to him, as regards both their general level of knowledge and their heroic past. How could he ever compete with those who had initiated and carried out the Revolution? And yet – the mere touch of his hand proved enough to bring down dozens of men covered in revolutionary glory.

From 1937 onwards his ascent was vertiginous. He turned out to be imbued with grace, with the most precious essence of everything most new and necessary.

With him, at least, everything seems cut and dried. It was by walking over other men's bones that this man became a deputy and a member of a Party committee.

But no, no. One should not be in too much of a hurry. One needs to think carefully, to understand everything before pronouncing judgement. For he too did not know – he knew not what he was doing.

Speaking in the name of the Party, his mentors once said to him, 'We're in trouble. We are surrounded by enemies. These men pretend to be tried-and-tested Party members, members of the pre-revolutionary underground, men who fought in the Civil War – but they are enemies of the people, secret agents, provocateurs . . .' The Party had told him, 'You are young and pure. I trust you, my son. Help me – otherwise I shall perish. Help me to conquer the forces of evil.'

Stamping its Stalinist boots, the Party had shouted at him, 'If you show the least indecision, you will prove that you are no different from these degenerates – and I will grind you to dust. Remember, you son of a bitch, that hut with no chimney, that black hut where you were born! It is I, the

Party, who am leading you towards the light. Revere loyalty and obedience! It is the great Stalin, your father, who gives you the order: "Tally-ho! Hunt them down!"'

No, no, he was not settling personal scores.

A Komsomol member from the country, he did not believe in God. The faith that lived in him was another faith: faith in the mercilessness of the chastising hand of the great Stalin. In him lived the unhesitating obedience of the believer. In him lived a blissful timidity before a powerful force, before this force's great guides and leaders: Marx, Engels, Lenin and Stalin. A foot soldier of the great Stalin, he acted on Stalin's orders.

Naturally, he did also feel a biological hostility, an instinctive secret loathing for the generation of intellectual and fanatical revolutionaries it was his role to hunt down.

He was carrying out his duty, he was not settling scores – but it was also out of an instinct for self-preservation that he wrote his denunciations. He was acquiring a capital more precious than gold or land: the trust of the Party. He understood that in Soviet life the trust of the Party was everything: power, honour, authority. And he believed that his lies served a higher truth: in his denunciations he could glimpse this Truth.

But can he be blamed when even better men than he were unable to make out what was a lie and what was the truth, when even pure hearts were powerless before the question: What is good and what is evil?

He believed, or rather, he wanted to believe – or rather, he couldn't not believe.

In some ways he disliked his dark work – except that it was his duty! And then again, in other ways his terrible work was attractive, seductive, intoxicating. 'Remember,' his mentors used to tell him, 'that you have neither father nor mother, neither brothers nor sisters. You have only the Party.'

It was a strange, troubling feeling: thoughtless obedience, far from rendering him powerless, endowed him with a terrible power.

In his curt, imperious voice, in his cruel eyes – the eyes of a military commander – one could sometimes sense a very different nature that lay hidden inside him: a crazed, stupefied way of being that had been nourished by centuries of Russian slavery, of Asiatic despotism . . .

But here too we must stop and think. It is a terrible thing to condemn even a terrible man.

And here we have a new comrade: Judas IV.

He lives in communal apartments; he is a minor to middling official; he is a collective-farm activist. But whoever he may be, his face is always the same. Whether he is old or young, whether he is ugly or a ruddy-faced giant of a Russian warrior, it is always easy to recognise him. He is a philistine, always greedy to acquire, fanatically devoted to his own material interests. His fanaticism – a fanaticism he displays in regard to the acquisition of a sofa bed, a bag of buckwheat, a Polish sideboard, imported textiles or construction materials that are in short supply – is equal in its intensity to the fanaticism of a Giordano Bruno or Andrey Zhelyabov.

He is the creator of a categorical imperative opposite to Kant's; for him, a man, and mankind as a whole, are simply means to be employed in the course of his never-ending hunt for objects. There is always a tense, hurt, irritated look in his eyes, whatever their colour. Someone has always just stepped on his toes; there is invariably someone he has to settle accounts with.

For him the State's passion for unmasking enemies of the people is a blessing. It is like a steady trade wind blowing across the ocean, a gracious following wind filling his small yellow sail. And at the price of the suffering of those he destroys, he gets what he needs: additional living space, a salary increase, a neighbour's hut, a suite of Polish furniture, a little garden, a heated garage for his Moskvich car . . .

He despises books, music, the beauty of nature, love and maternal tenderness. He wants objects, only objects.

But even he is not moved exclusively by material considerations. He is extremely touchy; his grievances fester inside him.

He will denounce a colleague who has made him jealous by dancing with his wife, a wit who has made fun of him during a dinner, even just someone from the communal apartment who has accidentally knocked into him in the kitchen.

He has two distinguishing features. First, he is a volunteer. No one frightened him into it; he writes denunciations of his own accord. Second, what he sees in a denunciation is the direct, definite material benefit that he can derive from it.

Nevertheless, let us restrain the fist that has been raised to strike him: his passion for objects is a passion born of poverty. Yes, he could tell you about a room eight metres square that is home to eleven people, where a paralysed man is snoring while a young couple rustle and moan beside him, where an old woman is muttering a prayer and a child who has wet himself keeps crying and crying. He could tell you about greenish-brown village bread made with ground-up leaves, and about a staple Moscow soup, made from frozen potatoes that were being sold off cheap, that he used to have three times a day.

He could tell you about a house without a single beautiful object; about chairs with plywood seats; about tumblers made of thick, murky glass; about tin spoons and two-pronged forks; about underwear mended many times over; about a dirty rubber raincoat that he had worn, in December, over a torn wadded jacket.

He could tell you about waiting for a bus on a dark winter morning, about the unimaginable crush in the tram after a night spent in a desperately cramped room.

It was, surely, living an animal life that had first engendered his animal passion for things, his longing for a more spacious den. The bestiality of his life had turned him into a beast.

Yes, yes, this is all true. But it is clear that he lived no worse than others. It is clear, in fact, that he lived better than many.

And these many, many others did not do what he did. Let us take our time; let us think – and only then pronounce judgement.

PROSECUTOR: Do you all confirm that you wrote denunciations against Soviet citizens?

INFORMERS: Yes, in a way.

PROSECUTOR: Do you admit that you are guilty of the deaths of innocent Soviet people?

INFORMERS: No, we categorically deny it. The State had already doomed these people. Our work was, one might say, cosmetic. It served to keep up appearances. Essentially, whatever we wrote and however we wrote it, whether we accused or defended them, these people were already doomed.

PROSECUTOR: But sometimes you wrote denunciations of your own free will. In such cases, you yourselves chose the victim.

INFORMERS: Our freedom of choice was only apparent. People were destroyed according to statistical methods. Those who belonged to particular social and ideological strata were scheduled for extermination. We were well aware of those parameters – and so were you. We never informed against members of social strata that were healthy and not already marked for destruction.

PROSECUTOR: Or in the words of the new Gospel: 'Push that

which is falling!'* Nevertheless, there were occasions, even during the harshest of times, when the State acquitted those you had slandered.

DEFENCE COUNSEL: Yes, there were indeed such occasions – because of mistakes. But only God makes no mistakes. And the fact that there were very few acquittals – as you well know – indicates that there were very few mistakes.

PROSECUTOR: Yes, you informers knew what you were doing. But please answer me: why did you inform?

INFORMERS (*in unison*): They forced me to, they beat me . . . I was hypnotised by terror, by the power of boundless violence . . . As for me, I was carrying out my duty as a Party member to the best of my understanding at the time.

PROSECUTOR: And you, Comrade Number Four, why aren't *you* saying anything?

JUDAS IV: Me? Why are you picking on me? I know, it's because I'm uneducated. Because it's easier for you to get the better of someone uneducated, someone with less understanding!

DEFENCE COUNSEL (*interrupting*): Please allow me to make a clarification. My client did indeed write denunciations in pursuit of personal ends. But please bear in mind that his personal interests were in no way at variance with those of the State. The State did not reject my client's denunciations. From this it can be deduced that he performed a service that was of use to the State, even though it may appear at first glance that he was impelled only by personal and egotistic considerations. And now – something more important still. In Stalin's day you too, comrade Prosecutor, would have been accused of underestimating the role of the State. Do you not understand that the force fields generated by our State – its heavy, multi-trillion-ton mass, the super-terror and super-submissiveness that it evokes in a speck of human dust – are such as to render meaningless any accusations directed against

71

a weak, defenceless, individual human being? It's absurd to blame a particle of fluff for falling to earth.

PROSECUTOR: Your own position is clear. You are reluctant to allow your clients to accept even a minimal share of guilt. Only the State, only the State is to blame. But what about you informers? What do you all think? Do you really not consider yourselves in the least to blame?

They exchange looks and whispers. A learned informer takes the floor.

INFORMER: Allow me to reply. For all its outward simplicity, your question is, in fact, far from simple. In the first place, it is pointless. What use is it now to attempt to find out who is guilty with regard to crimes committed in the era of Stalin? That would be like emigrating to the moon and then starting a lawsuit about title deeds to a plot of land here on earth. On the other hand, if we are to take the line that the two eras are not so distant from each other and that, *sub specie aeternitatis*, they stand 'almost side by side'* – as the poet said – then many other complexities arise. Why are you so eager to condemn those, like us, who are small and weak? Why not begin with the State? Why not try the State? *Our* sin, after all, is *its* sin. Pass judgement on the State then – fearlessly, out loud and in public. You have no choice but to be fearless – you claim, after all, to be speaking in the name of truth. Come on then, get on with it!

And please also explain one other thing. Why have you waited till now to raise these questions? You've known us all long enough. In Stalin's lifetime you were only too glad to spend time with us. You used to wait outside our offices for us to receive you. Sometimes you used to whisper about us in thin, sparrow-like voices. We too used to whisper like sparrows. Yes, like us, you participated in the Stalin era. Why must we, who were participants, be judged by you, who were also participants? Why must *you* determine *our* guilt? Do

72

you not see where the difficulty lies? Maybe we really are guilty, but there is no judge who has the moral right to discuss the question of our guilt. Remember how Leo Tolstoy said that no one in the world is guilty? But in our State things are different: everyone is guilty – there is not one innocent person anywhere. All that we can argue about is the degree of guilt. So is it for you, Comrade Prosecutor, to accuse us? Only the dead, only those who did not survive, have the right to judge us. But the dead do not ask questions; the dead are silent. So please allow me to answer your question with another question. I'm speaking to you straight-forwardly, man to man, from the heart, like a true Russian. What is the reason for this vile, universal weakness? Your weakness, our weakness, everyone's weakness? This mass submissiveness?

PROSECUTOR: You're evading the question.

Enter a secretary. He holds out an envelope to the learned informer, saying, 'Official.'

INFORMER (*after reading a sheet of paper, he holds it out to the prosecutor*): Please have a look. On the occasion of my sixtieth birthday, my more than modest achievements in the field of Soviet science have been recognised.

PROSECUTOR (*after reading the paper*): In spite of myself, I can't but be glad for you. We are, after all, all Soviet citizens.

INFORMER: Yes, yes, of course we are. Thank you. (*Muttering to himself*): Allow me, through the columns of your news-paper, to express my gratitude . . . to the institutions and organisations . . . and also to my comrades and friends . . .

DEFENCE COUNSEL (*striking a pose as he makes his final plea*): Comrade Prosecutor and you, sworn jurymen! The comrade prosecutor has accused my client of evading the question put to him: does he admit to even the least degree of guilt? But no more have you, Comrade Prosecutor, answered the question put by my client to *you*: what is the reason for our mass

73

submissiveness? Maybe it is human nature itself that has engendered informers, stool pigeons, writers of denunciations, collaborators with the security organs? Perhaps informers are born from the secretions of glands, from the pap slopping about our intestines, from the noise of gas in our stomachs, from mucous membranes, from the activity of the kidneys? Perhaps they are born from blind instinct – from the noseless, eyeless instinctual drives for nourishment, self-preservation and reproduction?

But anyway, isn't it all the same whether or not informers are to blame? Whether they are to blame or whether they aren't, what is loathsome is the fact that they exist. The animal, vegetable, mineral, physiochemical side of human beings is horrible. It is from this slimy, hairy, base side of human nature that informers are born. The State does not itself give birth to people. Informers have sprouted from man. The hot steam of State terror has breathed upon mankind and little grains that were sleeping have swollen and come to life. The State is the earth. If the earth has no grains lying hidden inside it, neither wheat nor tall weeds will grow from it. Humanity has only itself to blame for human filth.

But do you know the vilest thing of all about stool pigeons and informers? Do you think it is the bad in them?

No! The most terrible thing is the good in them; the saddest thing is that they are full of merits and good qualities.

They are loving and affectionate sons, fathers and husbands . . . They are capable of real achievements of virtue and labour.

They love science, our great Russian literature, fine music. Some of them can talk boldly and intelligently about the most complicated aspects of modern philosophy and art . . .

And what good, devoted friends one finds among them! How touching they can be when they visit a comrade who has been taken to hospital.

Among them are brave and patient soldiers who shared with their comrade their last crust of bread or last pinch of tobacco and who, in their own arms, carried a wounded, bleeding fighter off the field of battle.

And what gifted poets, musicians, physicists and doctors there are among them. What skilled craftsmen – metalworkers and carpenters – men who are spoken of with admiration as having 'golden hands'.

This is what is so terrifying; that there is so much good in them, so much good in their human essence.

Whom, then, should we judge? Human nature! Human nature is what engenders these heaps of lies, all this meanness, cowardice and weakness. But then human nature also engenders what is good, pure and kind. Informers and stool pigeons are full of virtue, they should all be released and sent home – but how vile they are! Vile for all their virtues, vile even with all their sins absolved . . . Who was it who made that cruel joke about the proud sound made by the word 'Man'?*

Yes, yes, dark saturnine forces compelled them. They were subjected to billion-ton pressures – and no one among the living is innocent. All the living are guilty . . . You, the defendant, are guilty, and you, the prosecutor, are guilty, and I, the writer – I who am thinking about the defendant, the prosecutor and the judge – am guilty.

But why is all this so painful? Why does our human obscenity make us feel such shame?

8

'What the hell made me decide to go on foot?' Pinegin kept asking himself. He had no desire to think about that dark bad something that had slept for decades and then suddenly awoken. Whether or not he had done wrong was not important; it was all just a matter of blind chance, of an unfortunate coincidence that had brought him face to face with a man he had ruined. Had they not bumped into each other on the street, the sleeper would have gone on sleeping.

But the sleeper had awoken, and Pinegin, though not quite realising this, was feeling less and less convinced by these thoughts about blind chance. He was feeling more and more troubled and regretful. 'No, it's true: it was me who snitched on Vanechka and – and I didn't need to. I destroyed the man, damn him! Otherwise we could have met today and everything would have been fine. Oh God, how grubby it all is. It's as if I'd reached into some lady's handbag, and she'd caught hold of my arm, and with my driver, my advisers, my secretaries all looking on . . . My God! How can one go on living when the whole world feels so dirty and grubby? Maybe my whole life is just vile and rotten. I should have lived it quite differently.'

And it was with a confused and heavy heart that Pinegin entered the Intourist* restaurant, where the maître d' and the doorman and the waiters had all known him for many years.

On catching sight of him, two cloakroom attendants sprang

out from behind a partition, calling 'Good day! Good day!' Prancing like young stallions, snorting with impatience, they stretched out their hands towards Pinegin's luxurious accoutrements. They were quick, sharp-eyed Russian boys from an Intourist restaurant cloakroom – boys with a precise memory for who had been there before, what he had been wearing and what he had happened to say. But they were, naturally, entirely open-hearted and spontaneous with Pinegin, treating him, with his badge of a deputy to the city soviet, almost as if he were their immediate superior.

Unhurriedly, sensing beneath his feet the soft yet resilient pile of the carpet, Pinegin made his way through to the restaurant. The room was spacious; it had high ceilings and was filled with a solemn half-light. Pinegin slowly breathed in the calm air, which was cool and warm at the same time, and looked around at the tables with their starched tablecloths; vodka glasses, wine glasses and cut-glass vases containing flowers were all gleaming softly. He made his way to a familiar and comfortable spot beneath the intricate foliage of a philodendron.

As he passed between little tables displaying the miniature flags of various world powers, he thought that these tables were like battleships and cruisers, and that he was like an admiral reviewing his fleet.

This sense of himself as an admiral made it easier to go on living, and he sat down at his table. Without hurrying, he reached for the dark olive-green menu that looked more like the certificate awarded to a laureate. Opening it, he focused on the section 'Hors d'Oeuvres'.

Examining the names of dishes, which were printed both in his native Russian and in other world languages, he turned over a stiff, crackling page, glanced at 'Soups', chewed his lips for a moment and then looked sideways at 'Meat Dishes' and 'Game Dishes'.

He hesitated, torn between Meat and Game. With perfect timing, guessing his predicament, the waiter pronounced, 'The fish and the sirloin are both exceptional today.'

Pinegin did not reply for a long time. 'All right then,' he said finally. 'Sirloin it is.'

He sat in the half-light and the quiet, his eyes half closed – and the full weight of his own sense of rectitude battled with the fire and ice of repentance, with the confusion and horror that had suddenly been resurrected within him.

Then the heavy velvet over the doorway into the kitchen gently parted and Pinegin recognised the bald head of a waiter – *his* waiter.

Out of the half-dark a tray was floating towards him, and Pinegin saw ash-pink salmon surrounded by small lemon suns, dusky caviar, the hothouse green of cucumbers, the steep sides of a vodka decanter and a bottle of 'Borzhomi' mineral water.

He was not really so very much of a gourmet, nor was he even feeling so very hungry, but it was at this precise moment that that old man, that old man in a padded jacket, ceased for a second time to trouble his sense of rectitude.

9

Back at the railway station, Ivan Grigoryevich began to feel that there was no point in wandering about Leningrad any longer. He stood inside the cold, high building and pondered. And it is possible that one or two of the people who passed the gloomy old man looking up at the black departures board may have thought, 'There – a Russian from the camps, a man at a crossroads, contemplating, choosing which path to follow.'

But he was not choosing a path; he was thinking.

During the course of his life dozens of interrogators had understood that he was neither a monarchist, nor a Social Revolutionary, nor a Social Democrat; that he had never been part of either the Trotskyist or the Bukharinist opposition. He had never been an Orthodox Christian or an Old Believer; nor was he a Seventh Day Adventist.

There in the station, thinking about the painful days he had just spent in Moscow and Leningrad, he remembered a conversation with a tsarist artillery general who had at one time slept next to him on the bed boards of a camp barrack. The old man had said, 'I'm not leaving the camp to go anywhere else. It's warm in here. There are people I know. Now and again someone gives me a lump of sugar, or a bit of pie from a food parcel.'

He had met such old men more than once. They had lost all desire to leave the camp. It was their home. They were fed at regular hours. Kind comrades sometimes gave them little scraps. There was the warmth of the stove.

Where indeed were they to go? In the calcified depths of their hearts some of them stored memories of the brilliance of the chandeliers in the palaces of Tsarskoye Selo,* or of the winter sun in Nice. Others remembered their neighbour, Mendeleyev, coming round to drink tea with them; or they remembered Scriabin, Repin or the young Blok. Others preserved, beneath ash that was still warm, the memories of Plekhanov, Gershuni and Trigoni, of friends of the great Zhelyabov. There had been instances of old men being released from a camp and asking to be readmitted. The whirl of life outside had knocked them off their feet. Their legs were weak and trembling, and they had been terrified by the cold and the solitude of the vast cities.

Now Ivan Grigoryevich felt like going back again behind the barbed wire himself. He wanted to seek out those who had grown so accustomed to their barrack stoves, so at home with their warm rags and their bowls of thin gruel. He wanted to say to them, 'Yes, freedom really is terrifying.'

And he would have told these frail old men how he had visited a close relative, how he had stood outside the home of the woman he loved, how he had bumped into a comrade from his student days who had offered to help him. And then he would have gone on to say to these old men of the camps that there is no higher happiness than to leave the camp, even blind and legless, to creep out of the camp on one's stomach and die – even only ten yards from that accursed barbed wire.

10

When he at last succeeded, after some difficulty, in finding himself a job and somewhere to live, Ivan Grigoryevich felt both peace and sadness. He had been taken on as a metal-worker in a small workshop that employed the disabled. The sacred stamp, that of a residence permit, appeared in his pass-port, and he began living in a small room that he rented for just forty old roubles a month from the widow of one Sergeant Mikhalyov, who had died in the war.

Anna Sergeyevna was thin and, although her hair was going grey, she was still young. With her lived her twelve-year-old nephew, the son of a sister who had died. He had a pale face and he went around in a jacket that had been much patched and darned. He was the kind of astonishingly quiet, timid and inquisitive boy that you find only in an extremely poor family.

On the wall there was a photograph of Sergeant Mikhalyov looking rather gloomy, as if he already foresaw his fate. Anna Sergeyevna's son was doing his military service – as a guard in a labour camp. A photograph of him, with fat cheeks and short, close-clipped hair, hung beside that of his father.

Sergeant Mikhalyov had gone missing during the first days of the war. His unit had been annihilated, not far from the frontier, by German tanks and there had been no one to give evidence as to whether Mikhalyov had been left on the battle-field, killed by sub-machine-gun fire, or whether he had surrendered to the Germans. And so the authorities had refused Anna Sergeyevna's application for a pension.*

Anna Sergeyevna worked as a cook, in a canteen. Nevertheless, she did not live well. Her elder sister, who worked on a collective farm, once sent her a food parcel for their orphaned nephew: round loaves made from rye flour and bran, and a jar of cloudy honey with bits of wax in it.

And if ever the chance arose, Anna Sergeyevna used, for her part, to send food parcels to her sister on the collective farm: flour, sunflower oil, and sometimes white bread and sugar.

Ivan Grigoryevich could not understand how, working in a kitchen, Anna Sergeyevna could be so pale and thin. Among a crowd of prisoners, it had always been easy to recognise the fat face of a cook.

Anna Sergeyevna did not ask Ivan Grigoryevich about his past in the camps. (He had been questioned at length by the workshop personnel officer.) But she was a woman of understanding – and she understood a great deal simply from observing Ivan Grigoryevich.

He was able to sleep on bare boards; he drank plain hot water with neither tea nor sugar; he ate plain bread without butter or margarine; he wore footcloths rather than socks.* He had no bed linen, but she noticed that his shirt collar was always clean, even though the shirt had been washed so many times that it had turned yellow. And in the mornings he always took out a chipped, battered little box that had once contained fruit drops and that now contained his washing things; he would brush his teeth and carefully soap his face, his neck and his arms up to his elbows.

He found it hard to get used to the silence at night. For decades he had been accustomed to a polyphony of snores; to all the snuffling, muttering and groaning of the hundreds of men asleep in the barrack; to the knocking of the nightwatchman's rattle or to the grinding of wheels of a prisoner transport train. He had been alone only in the punishment cell and during one period of the initial investigation, when he had been kept in solitary confinement for three and a half months. But the silence at night now was not the tense silence of solitary confinement.

He had been lucky to find the job in the workshop. In the town park he had got talking to a consumptive man whose back was so bent that it looked like a sledge runner standing on end, and this man had told him that he was giving up his job as a bookkeeper in a cooperative for the disabled and was going to leave the town. He was leaving, he explained, because he did not want to be buried in a town where the cemetery was located in a swamp and the coffins were all floating in water. He wanted to lie in comfort after his death. He had saved up for an oak coffin; he had bought some good-quality red cloth to line it, and he had also stocked up on brass-headed nails – the kind you see on the leather-upholstered benches in the railway station. He had no wish whatsoever to be soaking in water along with all these treasures.

He spoke about all this in the voice of a man about to move to a new, more comfortable apartment.

It was on the recommendation of 'the man with the new apartment', as he privately christened him, that Ivan Grigoryevich managed to get himself taken on at the cooperative, which produced locks and keys, as well as tinning and soldering kitchen utensils. Ivan Grigoryevich's past experience came in useful – at one time he had been a metalworker in a camp repair shop.

The other workers included injured veterans from the Great Patriotic War, as well as men who had been crippled in accidents in factories or on the roads and railways; there were even three old men who had been crippled as long ago as the First World War. There was also Mordan, another old-timer from the camps; he had formerly lived in Leningrad and worked in the Putilov factory.* He had been sentenced under Article 58* in 1936 and had been freed after the end of the war. Mordan did not want to return to Leningrad, where his wife and daughter had died during the Siege, and he had moved to this southern town to live with his sister.

The other workers were, for the main part, good-humoured people who preferred to look on the bright side of things. Now and again, however, one of them would have a fit, and his screams as he began to writhe on the floor would mingle with the banging of hammers and the squeal of files.

Ptashkovsky, a tinsmith with a grey moustache, had been taken prisoner by the Russians during the First World War (people said he was Austrian, just pretending to be a Pole). Suddenly his arms would go completely numb and he would freeze there on his little stool, his hammer raised in the air, his face immobile and haughty. Someone would have to shake him by the shoulder to bring him out of this paralysis. There had been an occasion when one man had a fit and this proved catching; in different corners of the workshop young and old alike had writhed on the floor and screamed.

One thing was very new for Ivan Grigoryevich: he was working as a free labourer, with no guards escorting him to his workplace, no sentries looking down from their watchtowers. This felt astonishingly good. It was also strange: the work was much the same, the tools were familiar, but no one called you a shit and neither *thieves* nor *bitches* threatened you or shook their bludgeons at you.

Ivan Grigoryevich quickly found out what people did to increase their meagre earnings. Some made teapots and saucepans out of materials they had bought themselves, selling them through the cooperative at the official price but keeping the money. Others made private agreements to do repair jobs for customers, not writing out any bills or receipts. Once again, they charged the official price, neither more nor less.

Mordan, a man whose hands looked big enough to be used for shovelling winter snow off the pavements, talked during one of their lunch breaks about an incident the previous day in the apartment next to his own. There were five tenants: a lathe operator, a tailor, an electrician who worked in a small factory and two widows. One of these widows worked in a sewing workshop, the other as a cleaner in the building of the town soviet. And then on one of their days off the two widows met unexpectedly in the police station; officers from the Department for the Struggle against Speculation and the Theft of Socialist Property had picked them up on the street for selling the string shopping bags that they wove at night in their rooms, neither saying a word to the other about what she was doing. The police then searched the apartment and discovered that the tailor was making boys' and women's coats at night. The electrician, for his part, had installed a small electric stove under the floorboards; on it he baked wafers that his wife sold in the market. As for the lathe operator from the 'Red Torch' factory, he turned out to be a night-time cobbler; his speciality was smart ladies' shoes. And the widows were not only weaving string bags but also knitting ladies' cardigans.

Mordan made his listeners laugh as he acted out, first, how the electrician had shouted that the wafers were for his family, and then, how the theft and speculation inspector had asked him how long his family would take to get through seventy pounds of dough. In the end, each speculator had been fined three hundred roubles. Each had been reported to his or her workplace – and each had been threatened with deportation, 'in order to purge Soviet life of parasites and unproductive elements'.

Mordan liked to use elevated words. Examining a damaged lock, he would say gravely, 'Yes, the key does not react at all onto the lock.'

Once, as they were walking down the street together after finishing work, Mordan suddenly said to Ivan Grigoryevich, 'It's not only because of my wife and daughter that I didn't go back to Leningrad. It's the Putilov proletariat... As a worker myself, I can't bear to see what's happened to them. They can't even go out on strike. How can we call ourselves workers if we don't have the right to strike?'

In the evenings Anna Sergeyevna would bring some food back for her nephew: some soup in a little tin can, a main course in an earthenware pot.

'Maybe you'd like something to eat?' she would say quietly to Ivan Grigoryevich. 'We've got plenty.'

'But you don't eat yourself,' Ivan Grigoryevich would reply. 'I've noticed.'

'I eat all day – because of my work,' she said once. Guessing what he was thinking, she went on, 'But I do get very tired.'

At first Ivan Grigoryevich had thought that there was something unkind about his landlady's face. Then he realised he had been wrong: she was a kind woman.

Sometimes she talked about life on the collective farm. She had been a brigade leader; for a while she had even been the farm chairman. She explained to him that the collective farms often failed to fulfil the plan. Too little land had been sown; or there would be a severe drought; or the land had been squeezed dry and it no longer yielded anything; or everyone except the old women and children had managed to escape to the city... And if a collective farm failed to deliver its quota of produce, then its members would receive only six or seven kopeks per labour-day,* plus a hundred grams of grain. And there were years when they did not receive even a single gram. And people don't like working for nothing . . . The collective farmers went about in rags. Clean black bread, without the addition of potatoes and acorns, was – like cake – something they ate only on special occasions. Once Anna Sergeyevna had brought her older sister some white bread, and her sister's children had been afraid to eat it; they had never seen white bread before. As for the peasants' huts, they were all falling apart – for lack of new timber.

Ivan Grigoryevich listened to Anna Sergeyevna and watched her. She gave off a soft light of kindness and femininity. For decades he had hardly seen any women, but what endless stories he had heard about them in the barracks. Sad stories, filthy stories, bloody stories. And the women in these stories were either so degraded as to be worse than animals or else so pure and sublime as to stand above the saints. But the prisoners had been no more able to do without their thoughts of women than they had been able to do without their ration of bread. Women had been with them all the time – in their talk, in the purest and in the dirtiest of their dreams and reveries.

Since his release Ivan Grigoryevich had seen beautiful, elegant women on the streets of Moscow and Leningrad, and he had sat at table with the grey-haired, still-beautiful Maria Pavlovna. But nothing – neither his grief on learning that the love of his youth had betrayed him, nor the charm of elegant female beauty, nor the sense of comfort and well-being in the home of Maria Pavlovna – nothing had made him feel what he felt as he listened to Anna Sergeyevna, as he looked at her sad eyes, at a face that might be faded but that was still sweet, still young.

But then this was not really so very strange. How could it be? It was simply what had always happened, what had happened for millennia, between a man and a woman.

Anna Sergeyevna went on talking about the collective farm.

'Forcing hungry people to go out and work in the fields became more than my soul could bear. Lenin may have been right to say that a cook can govern the State, but that certainly isn't true of me.* Women working on the threshing machine used to make themselves special stockings and sew them into the insides of their skirts. They used to fill these stockings with grain. It was my job to search them and start criminal proceedings against them. But the minimum sentence for theft of collective-farm property is seven years. And the women had children. I used to lie awake at night and think it all through: the State was taking grain from the collective farm for six kopeks per kilo and selling a loaf of bread for a rouble. And in *our* collective farm we hadn't been given so much as a gram of grain for four years. And if someone steals a fistful of grain – of the grain that they have, like it or not, sown themselves – they get seven years . . . No, I just couldn't go along with it. And so some fellow villagers got me a job here in a canteen, feeding people. Often I hear workers say, "In spite of everything, life's better here in the town." A construction worker gets two and a half roubles for hanging a door and putting in a lock. If he does the same job privately, on his day off, he gets paid fifty roubles. So he gets twenty-five times less from the State. All the same, the workers are right – the State really does take still more than that from the peasants. The way I see it, the State takes too much from everyone, both in towns and in villages. I know it has to pay for Houses of Recreation so that people can go on holiday, and for schools and tractors, and for defence . . . I do understand all that, but I still think it takes too much from all of us. It should take less.'

She looked at Ivan Grigoryevich. 'Is it possible,' she said, 'that this has thrown the whole of our lives out of kilter?'

She slowly turned her eyes from Ivan Grigoryevich's face to her nephew's and added, 'I do realise we're not meant to talk about these things. But I can see what kind of man you are. Otherwise, I wouldn't ask such a question. But you haven't the least idea what kind of person I am – so don't answer!'

'You don't need to say that,' said Ivan Grigoryevich. 'I certainly will answer. I used to think that freedom was freedom of speech, freedom of the press, freedom of conscience. But freedom needs to include all of the lives of all of the people. Freedom is the right to sow what you want. It's the right to make boots or shoes, it's the right to bake bread from the grain you've sown and to sell it or not sell it as you choose. The same goes for a locksmith or a steelworker or an artist – freedom is the right to live and work as you wish and not as you're ordered to. But these days there's no freedom for anyone – whether you write books, whether you sow grain or whether you make boots.'

That night Ivan Grigoryevich lay in the dark and listened to someone's sleepy breathing. The sound was so quiet that he could not make out whether it was the child's or the woman's.

He felt strange. It was as if he had been travelling all his life, as if night and day he had been in a creaking railway wagon, listening to the constant knock-knock of the wheels. And now at last he had arrived – the train had stopped.

And yet there was still a ringing in his ears. The din from those thirty years of travel was still echoing in his head. It seemed as if the prisoners were still in transit, still on their way . . .

But the noise in his head was not the noise of the railway. It was the grating sound of old age. How much longer, after all, did he have to live?

11

Alyosha, Anna Sergeyevna's nephew, was so short that he looked as if he were only eight years old. He was, however, already twelve; he was in his sixth year at school. After coming home, fetching the water and washing the dishes, he would sit and do his homework.

Sometimes he would look up at Ivan Grigoryevich and say, 'Could you test me on history, please?'

Once, when Alyosha was preparing for a biology lesson and Ivan Grigoryevich had nothing to do, he began moulding from clay the various animals shown in the textbook: a giraffe, a rhinoceros, a gorilla. Alyosha was dumbfounded – the clay animals were so splendid that he couldn't take his eyes off them. He couldn't stop moving them about; at night he arranged them on a chair next to his bed. At dawn, on his way out to go and queue for the milk, the boy saw Ivan Grigoryevich washing his face in the corridor. In an impassioned whisper he said, 'Ivan Grigoryevich, may I take your animals to school with me?'

'Please do – they're yours,' said Ivan Grigoryevich.

In the evening, Alyosha told Ivan Grigoryevich that the art teacher had said, 'Please tell your lodger that he really must go and study.'

This was the first time that Anna Sergeyevna had seen Ivan Grigoryevich laugh. She said, 'Don't laugh, go and see the woman. Maybe you can make some money at home in the evenings. After all, what kind of life can you have on three hundred and seventy-five roubles a month?'

'That's enough for me. What would I do with more?' said Ivan Grigoryevich. 'And as for studying, it's too late now. That's something I should have done thirty years ago.'*

But at the same time he was saying to himself, 'What am I getting so agitated about? – Does this mean I've still got some life in me? That I'm not dead yet?'

Once, Ivan Grigoryevich was telling Alyosha about the conquests of Tamburlaine when he noticed that Anna Sergeyevna had put down her sewing and was listening to him intently.

'You shouldn't be working in that workshop,' she said with a smile.

'I'd be no good anywhere else,' he said. 'My knowledge comes from books with half the pages torn out, with no beginning or end.'

Alyosha realised that this must be why Ivan Grigoryevich told stories his own way, while the teachers just ploughed through textbooks.

The little episode with the clay animals did indeed agitate Ivan Grigoryevich . . . Not that he had any real talent himself – but what a lot of deaths of talented people he had witnessed. Young physicists and historians, specialists in ancient languages, philosophers, musicians, young Russian Swifts and Erasmuses – how many of them he had seen put on their wooden jackets.

Pre-revolutionary literature had often lamented the fate of serf actors, musicians and painters. But who was there today to write about the young men and women who had never had the chance to write their books and paint their paint-ings? The Russian earth is indeed fertile and generous. She gives birth to her own Platos, to her own quick-witted Newtons* – but how casually and terribly she devours these children of hers.

Theatres and cinemas made Ivan Grigoryevich feel sad and anxious; it was as if he were being forced to watch the screen or the stage and would never be let out again. Many novels and poems felt like a violent assault, as if the writer were trying to drum something into his head; he found this unbearable. These books seemed to be about a life he had never encountered – a life where there were no barracks, no strict-regime camps, no brigade leaders, no armed guards, no security officers, no system of internal passports, and none of the sufferings, anxieties and passions that made up the lives of everyone around him.

The writers simply dreamed people up. They dreamed up their thoughts and feelings; they dreamed up the rooms they lived in and the trains they travelled in. The literature that called itself 'realist' was as convention-ridden as the bucolic romances of the eighteenth century. The collective farmers, workers and peasant women of Soviet literature seemed close kin to those elegant, slim villagers and curly-headed shepherdesses in woodland glades, playing on reed pipes and dancing, surrounded by little white lambs with pretty blue ribbons.

During his years in the camps Ivan Grigoryevich had learned a great deal about human weaknesses. Now he saw that there were more than enough such weaknesses outside the barbed wire as well as behind it . . . No, suffering did not always purify. In the camps the struggle for an extra mouthful of soup, for an easier work assignment, was unrelenting, and the morally weak stooped to a pitiful level. Sometimes Ivan Grigoryevich tried to guess how people he met now might behave in the camps; it was not difficult to imagine some sleek and haughty figure scavenging about, scraping his spoon round someone else's empty soup bowl or prowling around the kitchen in search of potato peelings or rotten cabbage leaves.

Ivan Grigoryevich had felt sorry for those who had been crushed by violence, by hunger and cold, by their desperate need for tobacco. He had felt sorry for those who had turned into 'camp jackals', always on the lookout for a crumb of bread or a slobbery cigarette butt.

What he had seen in the camps made it easier to understand how people behaved when they were free. What he observed now was the same pitiful weakness, the same cruelty, the same greed and the same terror that he had seen in the camps. People were the same everywhere, and Ivan Grigoryevich pitied them.

The role of the characters in Soviet novels and long poems, however, like that of the figures in medieval art, was to express the ideal of the Church, to proclaim the one true God: man existed not for his own sake but for God's sake, in order to glorify God and His Church. Some writers, those most adept at passing off lies as truth, took particular pains over the details of the clothes and furniture they described. They then peopled their realistic stage sets with idealised, God-seeking characters.

Neither within nor outside the camps were people willing to admit that everyone had an equal right to freedom. Some of the Right Deviationists believed themselves to be innocent but thought that it had been right to sentence the Left Deviationists. Left and Right Deviationists were alike in their hatred of 'spies' – of those who had corresponded with relatives abroad or who simply had Polish, Latvian or German surnames that they had inherited from Russified parents.

And however much the peasants insisted that they had worked all their lives by the sweat of their brow, the political prisoners refused to believe them. 'A likely story! Why would the authorities arrest a peasant unless he's exploiting others?'

Ivan Grigoryevich had once said to a former Red Army commander, his neighbour on the bed boards, 'You're a hero of the Civil War. You dedicated your whole life to the ideals of Bolshevism. And now here you are – sentenced for espionage!'

The man had replied, 'With me they made a mistake. There haven't been any others – I'm a special case.'

When the camp criminals picked on a new victim and began tormenting or robbing him, the political prisoners did nothing. Some looked the other way; some sat there with blank, unseeing faces; some ran away; others pulled blankets over their heads and pretended to be asleep.

Hundreds of political prisoners – hundreds of *zeks** – among whom were former soldiers and war heroes, had proved helpless against a small number of common criminals. The latter were a law unto themselves; they, after all, were true Russian patriots – unlike the 'Fascist' *zeks*, who were enemies of the motherland. The *zeks* were like dry grains of sand; there was no solidarity between them.

One man believed that the authorities had got it wrong in his case but that, in general, 'people aren't sent to the camps for nothing'.

Others reasoned as follows: 'When we were free, we thought that people aren't sent to the camps for nothing. Now, however, we know first hand that that *does* happen.' But they drew no conclusions; they merely sighed submissively.

An emaciated, compulsively twitching former official of the Youth Comintern, an expert in Marxist dialectics, explained to Ivan Grigoryevich that, even though he had committed no crimes against the Party, the security organs had been right to arrest him as a double-dealer and spy; although he himself had done nothing wrong, he belonged to a social stratum that was hostile to the Party, a stratum that spawned whiners and doubters, double-dealers, Trotskyists and 'opportunists in practice'.

An intelligent man, once an important Party official at the provincial level, said to Ivan Grigoryevich, 'When a forest is being felled, splinters fly – but the truth of the Party still holds. This truth is more important than my misfortune.' He then pointed to himself and added, 'So here I am – one of those splinters.'

He was at a loss for words when Ivan Grigoryevich replied, 'That's just it – they're felling the forest. Why do they need to fell the forest?'

Only very occasionally did Ivan Grigoryevich meet anyone who had actually done anything against the Soviet government.

Former tsarist officers had been sentenced not because they had formed monarchist organisations, but because it was thought that they *might* form monarchist organisations.

There were Social Democrats and Socialist Revolutionaries in the camps. Most had been arrested after they had ceased their political activities and become ordinary, loyal Soviet citizens. They had been arrested not for opposing the Soviet State but because it was thought possible that they *might* oppose it.

It was not for actually opposing the collective farms that peasants were sent to the camps. The peasants who were sent to the camps were those who *might*, under certain conditions, have opposed the collective farms.

People were sent to the camps for entirely innocent criticisms – for disliking the books and plays that had won State prizes or for disliking Soviet wireless sets and fountain pens. Might not such people, under certain conditions, become enemies of the State?

People were sent to the camps for corresponding with aunts or brothers who lived abroad. They were sent to the camps because there was a greater probability of their becoming spies than if they did not have such relatives.

State terror was directed not against those who had committed crimes but against those who, according to the security organs, were more likely to commit crimes.

Quite distinct from these people were those who really had fought against the Soviet government: elderly Socialist Revolutionaries, Mensheviks and anarchists; men who had fought for the independence of Latvia, Estonia, Lithuania and Ukraine; men who had fought under the command of Stepan Bandera.

The Soviet *zeks* looked on these men as their enemies. At the same time they could not help admiring men who had been imprisoned for an actual reason.

In one strict-regime camp, Ivan Grigoryevich met an adolescent schoolboy, Borya Romashkin, who had been sentenced to ten years. Borya really had written posters accusing the State of executing innocent people; he really had typed them out on a typewriter; he really had stuck them up at night on the walls of buildings in Moscow. Borya told Ivan Grigoryevich that during the investigation, dozens of KGB officers – among them several generals – had come to see him, all of them curious about this young lad who had been arrested for a genuine reason. In the camp, too, Borya was famous. Everybody knew about him; prisoners from neighbouring camps asked about him. When Ivan Grigoryevich was sent eight hundred kilometres to a new camp, he heard talk of Borya Romashkin the very first evening – his story had travelled all over Kolyma.

There was one surprising thing: people sentenced for a genuine reason, for active opposition to the Soviet State, believed that all political *zeks* were innocent – and that they should all of them, without exception, be freed. But those who had been framed, those who had been imprisoned on trumped-up charges – these millions of people tended to believe that only they themselves should be pardoned. They attempted to prove that all the falsely accused 'spies', 'kulaks' and 'saboteurs' were indeed guilty; they attempted to justify the brutality of the State.

There was one profound difference between people living in the camps and people living in freedom. People in the camps remained loyal to the time that had given birth to them. Different epochs of Russian life lived on in the thoughts, in the psychological make-up of each person. There were men who had taken part in the Civil War, with their own favourite songs, heroes and books; there were 'Greens';* there were followers of Petlyura with the still-raging passions of *their* time, with their own songs, poems and mannerisms. There were Comintern workers from the 1920s, with their own particular earnest enthusiasm, with their characteristic vocabulary and philosophy, with their particular demeanour and ways of pronouncing words. There were men who were really very old indeed – monarchists, Mensheviks, Socialist Revolutionaries – and who preserved within them a whole world of ideas, literary heroes and rules of conduct from some forty or fifty years ago.

In a ragged, cough-ridden old man you could instantly recognise a noble, though degraded and weak-willed, officer from a Guards regiment, and in the no less ragged man lying beside him on the bed boards, his face covered with the same grey stubble – an unrepentant Social Democrat. And in a stooped figure with a cushy job as a medical orderly you could glimpse a man who had been the commissar of an armoured train during the Civil War.

Elderly people living in freedom, on the other hand, were not marked by any such inimitable signs of their past. In them the past had been erased. They found it easy to adopt new ways of thinking and feeling and lived their lives in accordance with the present day; their vocabulary and thoughts, their passions, even their sincerest desires all changed submissively and compliantly, in tune with the course of events and the will of their superiors.

What is the reason for this difference? Is it that a man becomes frozen in the camps, as if under anaesthetic?

When he had been in the camps, Ivan Grigoryevich had constantly sensed people's natural longing to escape beyond the barbed wire, to return to their wives and children. But after his release, he sometimes met other former *zeks* – and their submissive hypocrisy, their fear of their own thoughts, their dread of being rearrested were so overwhelming that they seemed more truly and thoroughly imprisoned than when they had been doing forced labour.

Leaving the camp, working as a free labourer, living with his nearest and dearest, such a man would sometimes doom himself to a higher power of imprisonment, a more complete and profound imprisonment than anything he had been subjected to behind the barbed wire.

Nevertheless, in the torment, in the dirt and murk of camp life, it was freedom that was the light and strength of the prisoners' souls. Freedom was immortal.

In this small southern town, in the home of the widow of Sergeant Mikhalyov, Ivan Grigoryevich began to develop a broader, deeper understanding of the nature of freedom.

People's small, everyday struggles, the efforts made by workers to earn an extra rouble by moonlighting, the peasants' natural desire to fight for some of the bread and potatoes they had themselves grown – all this represented not only the wish for a more comfortable life, not only the wish to feed and clothe one's children well. The struggle for the right to make boots, to knit a cardigan, to sow what one wants to sow – all this was a manifestation of man's natural and indestructible aspiration towards freedom.

This aspiration was, he knew, no less indestructible in the souls of the *zeks*. On either side of the barbed wire freedom was immortal.

After work one evening he began making a mental list of items of camp vocabulary. There was, O God, a camp word for every letter of the alphabet. And you could write whole articles, narrative poems and novels about each of them.

Arest (arrest), *barak* (barrack) . . . all the way through to *yushka* (a kind of watery soup) and *zona* (the entire territory of the camp). A vast world with its own language,* its own economy and its own moral code. Yes, one could fill whole shelves with books about it – even more than with the countless volumes of Gorky's *History of Factories and Mills*.

There would be many areas of subject matter. One would be the story of prisoners' transports: how they were organised, the journey itself, how the prisoners were guarded . . . To one of today's prisoners the transports of the 1920s seem unbelievably naive and cosy. A compartment in a passenger train, a philosophically inclined guard who offers you pies to eat . . . The first timid buds of the world of the camps, a chick barely emerged from the egg, a bygone age . . .

Compare all that with a transport on its way to Krasnoyarsk today: a mobile prison city, made up of sixty four-axle goods wagons; tiny barred windows; three tiers of bed boards; store wagons; kitchen wagons; wagons for the guard dogs that roam round the train when it stops; carriages for the guards themselves . . . And the boss of the entire transport, surrounded like a fairy-tale pasha by whoring concubines and fawning cooks. And the inspections and headcounts . . . A supervisor climbs into the wagon while the other guards stand by the open doors, pointing their sub-machine guns at the *zeks* huddled together in one end of the wagon. The supervisor orders the *zeks*, one at a time, to the other end of the wagon – and however fast they move, he always manages to give them a blow with his stick, either on the arse or on the head.

And not long ago, after the Great Patriotic War, steel combs were installed underneath the tail wagon of each train. If a *zek* managed to dismantle the floorboards and throw himself prone between the rails, this comb would seize him, yank him up and hurl him underneath the wheels – no use, by then, to man or beast. And in case someone broke through the ceiling and climbed up onto the roof of a wagon, search-lights were installed on each train. From the locomotive to the very last wagon, their sharp beams pierced through the darkness – and if there was a man on the roof, the machine gun looking down the train knew only too well what to do. Yes, everything continues to evolve. The transport's economic system had also continued to perfect itself; there was surplus product everywhere. The guard officers were by then enjoying real comfort in the headquarters car; they and their men were receiving additional rations, levied from those intended for the dogs and the *zeks*, as well as being paid a large dis-placement allowance in consideration of the sixty days it took the transport to reach the camps of eastern Siberia. And each wagon saw its own economic processes, its own internal circulation of goods, its own harsh reality compounded of primitive accumulation and attendant pauperisation. Yes, everything flows, everything changes,* it is impossible to step twice into the same transport.

But who can describe the despair of this journey, this journey that took men from their wives? Who can describe the night-time confessions to the accompaniment of the creaks of the wagons and the iron clickety-clack of their wheels? Who can describe people's submissiveness and trustfulness in the course of this slow plunge into the abyss of the camps? Who can describe the *zeks'* letters – the letters the *zeks* threw from the dark of the goods wagons into the dark of the great mailbox of the Russian steppe, and which sometimes, unbelievably, reached their destination?

In the train everything is unfamiliar. You have yet to develop camp habits. Your body is not exhausted, your mind is not dazed by the many concerns of camp life. Your heart is raw and bleeding. Everything is strange and terrible: the half-dark, the creaking, the rough boards, the hysterical twitching *thieves*, the quartz-like stare of the guards.

Ivan remembered a young boy being lifted up to the little window. He shouted out, 'Grandad, Grandad, where are they taking us?'

And everyone in the goods wagon heard an old man reply in a cracked, drawn-out voice, 'To Siberia, dear child, to forced labour.'

And Ivan Grigoryevich suddenly said to himself, 'Did all this really happen to me? Has this been my journey, my fate? It was with those transports that my road began. And now it has reached its end.'

These camp memories kept flooding back. There were no links between them, and this chaotic quality was painful and tormenting. But he felt, he knew that it was possible to make sense of this chaos, that this was not beyond him. His journey through the camps was now over and it was time to see clearly, time to discern the laws of this chaos of suffering where guilt was juxtaposed with holy innocence, where false confessions to crimes lived alongside fanatical loyalty to the Party, where senseless absurdity – the murder of millions of innocent and loyal people – masqueraded as cast-iron logic.

12

Ivan Grigoryevich had said very little during the last few days. He had hardly spoken to Anna Sergeyevna. But he had thought a lot about her and about Alyosha when he was at work, and he was always looking at the small pendulum clock on the wall: how much longer till he could go home?

And for some reason, during these days that he spent quietly thinking about life in the camps, what he found himself dwelling on was the fate of the camp women . . . Never, it seemed, had he thought so much about women.

It is not universities and works of sociology that have affirmed women's equality with men. It is not only factory work, space flight and the fire of revolution that have proved this equality. In the history of Russia this equality has been established now and always, forever and ever, by the suffering of serfdom, the suffering endured in prisons and transports, the suffering in the camps.

The centuries of serfdom, the camps of Kolyma, Norilsk and Vorkuta, all declare that woman has become the equal of man.

The camps also confirmed a second truth, a truth as simple as one of the commandments: the lives of men and women cannot be separated.

There is satanic power in a prohibition, in a dam. The water of streams and rivers, blocked by a dam, reveals a dark, secret power. This power can be concealed for a while by melodious splashes, by the play of sunlight on water, by swaying water lilies – but all of a sudden the water's implacable fury is crushing stone or driving the blades of a turbine with delirious speed.

When a barrier separates human beings from their daily bread, the power of hunger becomes no less pitiless. The natural and benign need for food turns cruel and bestial; it becomes a force that destroys millions of lives and compels mothers to eat their own children.

The prohibition that separates men and women in the camps warps their bodies and warps their souls.

A woman's tenderness, her readiness to care for others, her sexual passion, her maternal instincts – all this constitutes the bread of life, the water of life. All this is engendered in a woman because there are husbands, sons, fathers and brothers in the world. And that the world contains wives, daughters, mothers and sisters fulfils the life of a man.

But then a prohibition arises. And everything simple and good – the bread of life and the water of life – suddenly becomes dark and evil.

Like some act of sorcery, a prohibition imposed by force invariably transforms what is good within a human being into something evil.

Between the camps for male and female common criminals there always lay a strip of bare earth, known as the 'shooting zone'. The moment anyone appeared in this no-man's-land, machine guns would open fire. Nevertheless, the male criminals would try to creep across on their bellies; they would dig tunnels; they would try to slip under or over the barbed wire; and those who were unlucky were left lying on the ground with broken legs and bullet holes in their heads. It was like the frantic, tragic struggle of spawning fish to make their way up a river that has been blocked by dams.

In some strict-regime camps the women had not seen a

man's face or heard a man's voice for many years. There were occasions when carpenters, metalworkers and drivers were sent into these sinister places – and torn apart, tortured to death. Even the male criminals were terrified of these camps – camps where it was considered a joy merely to touch the shoulder of a dead man with one hand. The criminals were scared to go there even under armed guard.*

Dark, sombre misery twisted and mutilated human beings, until they ceased to be human.

Women forced other women into concubinage. The camps created a new, absurd breed of woman: fearsome dykes with hoarse voices, women with bold gestures and long male strides, women who wore trousers that they tucked into soldiers' tarpaulin boots. And at their side were their lost, pathetic *chicks*.

The dykes drank *chifir** and smoked *makhorka*. When they were drunk, they would beat up their frivolous, cheating girlfriends, but they also used their fists and their knives to protect these girlfriends from insult, or from anyone else's advances. Such was the nature of love in a labour camp – tragic and monstrous. Even among the criminals and murderers these relationships did not inspire laughter or dirty jokes – only fear and horror.

The frenzy that was labour-camp love did not recognise the vast distances of the taiga; it ignored the barbed wire, the stone walls of the guardhouse, the locks of the disciplinary barracks; it flung itself against wolfhounds, against knife blades, against the guards' rifles. It did indeed recall salmon coming up from the ocean to spawn – their backbones broken, their eyes half out of their sockets, yet still hurling themselves against the rocks and boulders of mountain rapids and waterfalls.

And at the same time men cherished the love of their wives and their mothers. And camp 'correspondence brides', who had never seen and never would see the camp 'grooms' they had chosen, were prepared to endure any suffering in order to remain faithful to their dispossessed chosen one, to remain faithful to illusions they had dreamed up.*

A lot can be forgiven anyone who, amid the filth and stench of camp violence, remains a human being.

13

Dear, quiet little Mashenka . . . She is no longer wearing her fine stockings and her blue woollen cardigan. It's hard to keep neat and tidy in a goods wagon. She keeps listening intently to the strange language – it hardly even sounds like Russian – of the women thieves who are her neighbours on the bed boards. She looks with horror at the transport tsaritsa, the pale-lipped, hysterical mistress of a famous Rostov *thief*.*

Masha washes her handkerchief in a mug. Then she uses the last drops of water to clean her feet, spreads the kerchief out on her knees to dry and peers into the half-dark.

The last few months are a blurred fog: little Yulia's tears after eating too much on her third birthday; the faces of the men carrying out the search; clothes, technical drawings, dolls and dishes strewn about the floor; the rubber plant, a wedding present from her mother, torn out of its pot; her husband's smile as he stood in the doorway for the last time, a pathetic, pleading smile, imploring her to remain loyal, a smile she could not remember without crying out and clasping her head in her hands; then mad weeks when everything went on just the same, little Yulia's saucepan of porridge coexisting with the glacial horror of the Lubyanka; the queues at the reception office of the internal prison, and a voice from the little window saying, 'Your parcel is refused'; the scurrying around to see various relatives; learning their addresses by heart; the hurried, clumsy sale of a wardrobe with a mirror and a set of the fine volumes published by Academia; the pain she had felt when a beloved friend had stopped phoning her; more night-time guests and a search that had gone on until dawn; saying goodbye to little Yulia, whom they would almost certainly have sent to an orphanage rather than allowing her grandmother to take charge of her; a cell in the Butyrka* where everyone spoke in whispers, and where matches and fish bones picked out of the gruel served as needles for doing one's mending; the colourful sight of dozens of hand-kerchiefs, knickers and bras all being waved in the air to dry; a midnight interrogation during which, for the first time in her life, a man shook his fist at her, addressing her as '*ty*' and calling her a whore and a prostitute. She was charged with failing to denounce her husband, who, for his part, had been sentenced to 'ten years without right of correspondence'* for failing to denounce 'terrorists'.

Masha did not understand why she and dozens like her had been expected to denounce their husbands, why Andrey, and hundreds like him, had been expected to denounce their work colleagues and childhood friends. She was questioned by the investigator only once. This was followed by eight months of prison: day and night, night and day. Despair would give way to a dazed waiting for fate; now and again, as if by an ocean wave, she would be swept up by hope, by a certainty that she would soon see her husband and daughter.

Finally, the jailer handed her a thin slip of cigarette paper on which she read, '58–6–12'.*

Even after this she kept hoping. Her sentence would be repealed – yes, her husband had been acquitted, Yulia was already back at home and soon they would meet, never to be separated again. The thought of this reunion made her turn hot and cold with joy.

She was woken in the middle of the night. 'Lyubimova,

with your belongings – quick!' She was taken in a Black Maria not to the Krasnopresnenskaya transit prison but straight to the freight terminus for the Yaroslavl line, to be put on a prisoners' transport . . .

She remembered the morning after her husband's arrest with particular clarity, as if that morning were still continuing. The main door to the building had slammed shut; there had been the sound of a car driving away, then silence. Terror had entered her soul. The telephone was ringing in the corridor; the lift was suddenly stopping on their floor; a neighbour was shuffling out of the kitchen, and then her shuffling unexpectedly stopped.

She wiped the books scattered about the floor with a cloth and put them back on their shelves. She tied the linen lying on the floor into a bundle. Really she would have liked to boil it – everything in the room seemed to have been fouled. She put the rubber plant back into its pot and stroked one of its leathery leaves. Andryusha had made fun of this plant, saying it was a symbol of philistinism, and deep down she had agreed with him. Nevertheless, she had always defended it and never allowed her husband to move it out into the kitchen. She did not want to hurt her poor mother who, already an old woman, had carried it all the way across Moscow and had even had to drag it up to the fourth floor, since the lift had been under repair at the time.

Everything was silent. But their neighbours were not asleep. They pitied her, they were afraid of her, and they were over-joyed that no one had come to *their* room with search and arrest warrants . . . Little Yulenka was asleep, and she was tidying the room. Ordinarily she did not worry so much about tidiness. By and large she was indifferent to material things; she had never cared about chandeliers or beautiful china. Some people thought her slovenly, a bad housewife. But Andrey liked Masha's indifference to objects and the general disorder of their room. Now, though, she felt that if things regained their proper places, she would feel calmer and less oppressed.

She glanced in the mirror and looked round the room she had tidied. *Gulliver's Travels* was back where it had been yesterday, before the search. The rubber plant was back on its little table. And Yulia, who had been weeping and clinging to her mother until four in the morning, was asleep. It was quiet in the corridor; their neighbours were not yet making a noise in the kitchen.

And in her now properly tidied little room Masha felt lacerated by despair. Her heart felt bright, glowing with love and tenderness for Andrey, but at the same time, in this domestic calm, surrounded by familiar objects, she sensed as never before a merciless force capable of bending even the very axis of the earth. This force had attacked her; it had attacked Yulia and the small room about which she had said, 'I don't even want twenty square metres and a balcony, because I'm happy where I am.'

Yulia. Andryusha. She was being taken away from them. The clickety-clack of the wheels was drilling into her heart. She was moving ever further from Yulia. Every hour was taking her closer to Siberia – to whatever had been given her in exchange for a life with those whom she loved.

Dear Mashenka was no longer wearing her checked skirt. And the woman *thief* with the pale thin lips was combing her crackling, electric hair with Mashenka's comb.

Only in the heart of a young woman can these two terrible torments live side by side: a mother's desperate longing to save her helpless child – and a child's helplessness before the fury of the State, a child's wish to hide her face in her mother's breast.

Her dirty, broken fingernails had once been manicured. Little Yulia had been intrigued by their colour, and her father had once said to her, 'Mummy's fingernails are like the scales of a little fish.' There was no longer any trace of a wave in her hair. She had had her hair done a month before Andryusha's arrest, when they were getting ready for the birthday party of the friend who no longer telephoned her.

Little Yulenka, dear shy, anxious little Yulenka – in an orphanage. Masha let out a quiet, plaintive groan and her eyes clouded over: how could she protect her little daughter from cruel orphanage attendants, from vicious children, from coarse, ragged orphanage clothing, from army blankets and prickly, straw-stuffed pillows? And the wagon kept creaking; there was no end to the clickety-clack of the wheels. Moscow and Yulia were ever further away from her; Siberia was drawing closer and closer.

Good God, had her Moscow life ever really existed? But a moment later it was the present that seemed like a dream, like a nightmare: this stifling half-dark, this aluminium bowl, the women *thieves* smoking their *makhorka* on the rough boards, her dirty underwear, her itching body, the anguish in her heart: 'If only we stop soon – then at least the guards will protect us from the *thieves* . . .' And then, at each stop, the terror she felt as the guards swore and waved the butts of their rifles about. All she could think was: 'If only the train could get going again . . .' Even the *thieves* had said, 'Those Vologda guards are worse than death.'

But Masha's deepest pain had nothing to do with the creaking bed boards, or the frost that covered the walls the moment the stove went out, or even the brutality of the guards and the savagery of the *thieves*. Her deepest pain was that she was now emerging from the numbness that had cocooned her soul during her eight months in the prison cell.

This 9,000-kilometre descent into the deep grave of Siberia was something she sensed with every cell of her being.

In the transport there was no place for the senseless hope she had had in prison that the cell door would suddenly open and a guard would shout, 'Lyubimova, get your things! You're free!' And that she would go out onto Novoslobodskaya Street, catch a bus home and find Andrey and Yulia waiting for her there.

In a transport, there is neither the numbness of the prison cell, nor the mindless exhaustion of the camps – only the ache of a battered heart.

And what if Yulia wet her knickers? Was she washing her hands? And her nose? Did it need blowing? And what about vegetables? She really needed her green vegetables. And she was always throwing off the bedclothes at night – often she ended up quite naked.

Mashenka was no longer wearing her own shoes; instead she had soldiers' boots, one of which had a torn sole. Was this really her – Maria Konstantinovna, who used to read Blok, who had studied literature, who, without ever telling Andrey, had written poetry of her own? Masha, who used to rush to the Arbat* to make an appointment with Ivan Afanasyevich, the hairdresser they all called 'Jean'? Masha, who had not only read books but who could also sew, make borsch, bake torte Napoleon, and who had breastfed a child? Masha, who had always been so full of admiration for Andrey, for his modesty and the energy he put into his work? Masha, who had won everyone's admiration for her devotion to her husband and daughter? Masha, who knew how to weep, and who knew how to be witty, and who was good at looking after the pennies?

And the train continued on its way, and now Masha had the first stages of typhus. Her head felt clouded, dark, heavy. But no, it was not typhus, she was all right. And once again hope found a path to her heart. They would reach the camps, and someone would call out her name: 'Lyubimova, step forward. There's a telegram for you. You're released.' And so on and so forth – and she would go by passenger train to Moscow . . . The city suburbs . . . Sofrino . . . Pushkino . . . The Yaroslavl station . . . And Andrey, holding Yulia in his arms.

And hope brought heartache. If only they could get to their destination sooner, if only she could get that telegram sooner . . . Yulia's thin little legs were moving so quickly. The carriage was slowing down now, and Yulia was running alongside it.

At last, after the *thieves* have stolen every last possession of hers, Masha gets off the train. Around her head she is wearing a dirty, shaggy towel, and she is hiding her freezing fingers in the sleeves of a greasy padded jacket. And squeaking glassily over the snow are the shoes of hundreds of Moscow women, all of them sentenced to ten years of hard labour for failing to denounce their husbands.

Their legs are still clad in silk stockings; their high-heeled shoes keep tripping. These women are envious of Masha. She travelled in a wagon with *thieves* and not with other wives. Her own clothes have all gone, but she has a padded jacket instead – and boots she can stuff with paper and rags to keep her feet warm.

These wives of enemies of the people stumble, hurry forward, fall to the ground. They quickly gather up their little bundles, which have scattered over the snow, but they are afraid to cry.

Masha looks round: behind her is the station shed, and a string of goods wagons that look like red beads against snow-white skin; in front of her slowly uncoils a long column of female prisoners, like a dark snake; all around are stacks of timber, powdered with snow. And there are the guards in their marvellously warm sheepskin coats – and the incessantly barking guard dogs in their own warm, thick fur.

The air, after two months in the transport, is intoxicatingly clean, but it feels sharper than a razor blade. The wind gets up; a dry, snowy cloud billows over the open ground, and the head of the column is lost in a white blur. The cold whips faces and legs. Masha's head whirls.

And all of a sudden, through her exhaustion, through her fear of frostbite and gangrene, through dreams of finding herself somewhere warm, of being taken to a bath-house to wash, through her confusion at the sight of a portly old woman in pince-nez glasses, lying on the snow with a strange, stupidly capricious look on her face – through all of this, and through the snowy mist, twenty-six-year-old Masha glimpsed her camp future. Far behind her, thousands of miles away, she could see her Moscow past, in a building on Spasopeskovsky Lane – a life now closed up and sealed. But here, emerging out of the mist were watchtowers, guards in full-length sheepskin over-coats, wide-open gates. At this moment Masha saw both her lives with equal clarity: a fate that had gone, and a fate that had come.

She runs, stumbles, blows on her icy fingers. She is still gripped by the delirium of hope. Soon she'll get to the camp – and they'll tell her about her release. She runs fast; she gets out of breath.

How hard she had to work. How her stomach hurt, how the small of her back ached from the incredible weight – far beyond what was acceptable for a woman – of the great chunks of lime. Even when they were empty, the hand-barrows felt as if they were made of cast iron. Everything was heavy: the spades, the crowbars, the boards, the logs, the vats of dirty water, the latrine barrels full of excrement, the piles of dirty laundry that weighed tens of kilos.

How hard it was to walk to work in the predawn dark-ness. How hard it was to endure the inspections, standing in the slush, or in freezing cold. How she longed for the nauseating maize swill containing a scrap of tripe or fish scales that stick to the roof of your mouth. How pitilessly the *thieves* stole. What sordid conversations she heard at night on the bed boards. What horrible fumblings, whisperings and rustlings. How eternally she longed for the stale, slightly greying black bread.

Sixteen-year-old Lena Rudolf, Masha's neighbour on the bed boards, began sleeping with Mukha,* the criminal who looked after the boiler room. Lena caught syphilis from him. She lost her hair and her fingernails and was then transferred to a camp for the disabled. Lena's mother, the kind, obliging, blue-eyed Susanna Karlovna, somehow remained as elegant as ever. Even though her hair was now grey, she still went on working, doing exercises every morning before dawn and rubbing herself down with snow.

Masha worked every day until dark, like a mare, like a she-donkey or a she-camel. It was a strict-regime camp, and she did not have the right to send or receive letters. She did not know whether her husband was still alive or whether he had been executed. She knew nothing about her little Yulia. Had she ended up in an orphanage, or had she simply got lost like some small animal with no name? Perhaps her mother had, after all, managed to find Yulia? But was her mother still alive? Was her brother Volodya still alive? She seemed to have grown used to knowing nothing about her nearest and dearest. She seemed to have stopped dreaming about receiving a letter. All she wanted, it seemed, was easier work, a job in the hospital or the kitchen – anything so as not to have to go out into the taiga, amid the terrible cold or the clouds of mosquitoes.

But her longing for her husband and daughter was as strong as ever, and her hope had not died; it only seemed to have died. Hope was sleeping. And to Masha her hope was like a little child asleep in her arms; when hope awakened, her heart filled with happiness, light and grief.

One day she would see Yulia and her husband again. Not today, of course, and not tomorrow. The years would pass, but she would see them again. 'Your hair's turned grey, Andrey . . . How sad your eyes look . . .' And Yulenka, dear little Yulenka. This pale, thin young woman was her daughter. But then came worrying thoughts: Would Yulia recognise her? Would she remember her, her camp mother? Or would she turn away from her?

Semisotov, one of the senior guards, forced her to sleep with him. He knocked out two of her teeth and struck her on the temple. This was during her first autumn in the camp. She tried to hang herself, but failed; the rope was too weak. Some of the women, however, even felt envious of her. Then came a kind of pained indifference. Twice a week she dragged herself along, behind Semisotov, to a storeroom where there were bed boards covered with sheepskins. Semisotov was always sullen and silent and she would be out of her mind with fear. When he was drunk and furious, she would feel sick with terror. But once he gave her five sweets and she thought, 'If only I could send them to Yulia in her orphanage.' Instead of eating them, she hid them in her little straw mattress. They were stolen. Once Semisotov said to her, 'You're filthy, you slut. No peasant woman would ever let herself get so dirty.' Surprisingly, he always addressed her as '*vy*', even when he was dead drunk. Semisotov's disgust gladdened her, but at the same time she thought, 'If he ditches me, it'll be back to carrying loads of quicklime.'

One evening Semisotov left the barrack and never came back. She learned later that he had been transferred to another camp. And she was glad to be able to sit on the bed boards in the evening – glad not to have to follow him, hanging her head, to the storeroom. But then she was thrown out of the office building where, in the days of Semisotov, she had cleaned floors and kept the stoves going. She had nothing to offer by way of a bribe, and so her place was taken by the *thief* who had stolen her woollen cardigan in the transport. Masha was glad that Semisotov had gone, but she also felt hurt. He had not said even a word of goodbye to her; he had treated her worse than a dog. And she was a woman who had once had a Moscow residence permit. She and her husband and Yulia had had a room of their own. She had washed in a bathroom; she had eaten from a plate.

And her work was very hard during the winter months. And it was hard in summer, and in spring, and it was hard in autumn, and now she no longer remembered the Arbat or her husband but only how, in the days of Semisotov, she had cleaned floors in the office building. Had she really been blessed with such good fortune?

Nevertheless, hope persisted, living its secret life inside her: they would all see each other again. By then, of course, she would be an old woman. Her hair would be quite grey, and Yulia would have children of her own – but they would see each other again. They simply couldn't not.

There were so many worries, so many things that needed attending to: a torn shirt; an outbreak of boils; a pain in her stomach – and she was refused permission to go to the doctor. One day the skin on her heels started tearing, and then she was limping, and her footcloths were black with blood. Then one of her felt boots was falling apart. Then she was desperate to wash herself and her things; she simply had to go to the bathhouse at once, even if it were only for a few minutes, without waiting for the day when it would be her turn. Then she had to find a way of drying her padded jacket, which had got soaked in the rain . . . And it was a struggle to get hold of every smallest thing: a tin of hot water; a length of darning thread; a needle she could rent; a spoon with an intact handle; a scrap of material to use as a patch. And how could she escape from the gnats? How could she protect her face and hands from the cold – a cold as vicious as the camp guards?

The prisoners' cursing and swearing, their fights and quarrels were no easier to bear than the work.

Life in the barrack went on.

Auntie Tanya, who had once lived in Oryol and worked there as a cleaner, used to whisper, 'Grief to those who live on this earth!' She had a coarse face, more like a man's; it looked cruel and frenzied. But there was not the least hint of cruelty or frenzy in Auntie Tanya, nothing but kindness. Why had this saint been sent to the camp? With an incomprehensible meekness, she was always ready to help out, to take someone else's place washing floors or doing some other routine task in the barrack.

The two old nuns, Varvara and Ksenya, would exchange quick whispers the moment any sinner approached them. Then they would fall silent. They lived in a world apart. To sign any document was a sin; to utter their worldly name was a sin; to drink from the same mug as a woman of the world was a sin; to put on a camp jacket was a sin. They would die rather than do any of these things – so stubbornly did they cling to their holiness. Their holiness was visible in their clothes, in their white kerchiefs, in their pursed lips, but in their eyes was only cold indifference – and contempt for the sins and sufferings of the camps. Their celibate souls were repelled by womanly passions and troubles, by the sufferings of mothers and wives; they looked on all such things as unclean. What mattered was to preserve the cleanliness of your kerchief, of your cup, to purse your lips and keep your distance from the sinful life of the camp. The *thieves* hated them, and the 'wives' disliked and avoided them too.

Wives, wives, wives, from Moscow and from Leningrad,

from Kiev, Kharkov and Rostov; sad women, down-to-earth women and unworldly women; sinful, weak, meek and spiteful women; women who laughed a lot; Russian and non-Russian women – and all of them wearing their camp jackets. The wives of doctors and engineers, of artists and agronomists; the wives of Marshals of the Soviet Union, and the wives of chemists; the wives of public prosecutors and of the dispossessed peasants who had grown grain throughout Russia, the Ukraine and Belorussia. All of them had been led by their husbands into the Scythian dark of the burial mounds known as camp barracks.*

The more famous the enemy of the people who had perished, the wider the circle of women he dragged down: his wife, his ex-wife, his very first wife, his sisters, a secretary, a daughter, a close friend of his wife, a daughter from his first marriage.

Of some it was said, 'She's surprisingly modest and un-assuming.' Of others, 'Oh, she's quite unbearable. So high and mighty – anyone would think she was still in possession of all her Kremlin privileges!' The latter had their toadies and dependants even here. Over them hung an aura of power and doom. People repeated in a whisper, 'No, you can be sure *they* won't get out of here alive.'

There were old women with calm, tired eyes who had first been imprisoned way back in Lenin's day and who had served whole decades in the prisons and camps. Members of the People's Will, Social Democrats and Socialist Revolutionaries. These women were treated with respect by the guards, and even by the *thieves*. They did not get up from the bed boards even if the camp superintendent himself came into the barrack. People said that one of them, Olga Nikolaevna, a little old woman with grey hair, had been an anarchist before the Revolution; she had thrown a bomb at the carriage of the governor of Warsaw and had fired a shot at a police general. And now here she was – sitting on the bed boards, reading a book and drinking a mug of hot water. One night Masha had returned from a visit to the storeroom with Semisotov and this old woman had come over to her, stroked her head and said, 'My poor girl!' How Masha had cried.

Susanna Karlovna Rudolf's place on the bed boards was not far from Masha's. She was still doing her exercises, still taking care always to breathe through her nose. Her Christian Socialist husband, a German American, had come to Soviet Russia with his family and taken Soviet citizenship. Professor Rudolf had been sentenced to 'ten years without right of correspondence', that is, he had been shot in the basement of the Lubyanka. Susanna Karlovna and her three daughters – Agnessa, Luiza and Lena – had been sent to strict-regime labour camps. She knew nothing at all about her elder daughters, and it was now some time since Lena, the youngest, had been sent to the camp for the disabled. Susanna Karlovna no longer exchanged greetings with Olga Nikolaevna – not since Olga Nikolaevna had called Stalin a Fascist and Lenin the assassin of Russian freedom. Susanna Karlovna said that through her work she was helping to construct a new world and that this gave her the strength to endure the separation from her husband and daughters. When she was living in London, she had known H. G. Wells, and in Washington she had met President Roosevelt, who had enjoyed talking to her husband. She accepted everything; she understood everything. Only one thing did she not quite understand: the man who had come to arrest her husband had pocketed a large and very rare gold coin; it was almost the size of a child's hand and it was worth a hundred dollars. On it was a silhouette of a Red Indian with a feathered headdress. The officer must, she thought, have taken it for his little son, not even realising it was gold . . .

All of them – the pure and the fallen, the most robust

and the most exhausted – inhabited a world of hope. Hope sometimes slept, sometimes awoke, but it never left them.

Masha too had hope. Hope tormented her; but even as it tormented her, hope made it possible for her to breathe.

The Siberian winter, itself almost as long as a term in the camps, was followed by a pale spring. Masha and two other women were sent to clear the road to the 'socialist settlement' where the camp bosses and the free employees lived in log cottages.

What she saw from a distance was the silhouette of a rubber plant and her own Arbat curtains in the high windows. She saw a little girl with a school satchel climb up onto the porch and enter the house belonging to the officer in charge of the administration of the strict-regime labour camps.

Their guard said, 'What d'you think you're here for – to watch a film?'

And on their way back in the last of the evening light, as they passed the timber store, they suddenly heard the sound of Radio Magadan.*

Masha and the two other women dragging themselves along through the spring mud put their spades down and stopped.

Silhouetted against the pale sky were the camp watchtowers. The guards in their black coats were like huge motionless flies. As for the squat barracks, it was as if they had just emerged from the earth and were now thinking better of it, wondering if they should sink down into it again.

It was not sad music but merry; it was dance music. Listening to it, Masha wept as she seemed never to have wept in all her life. And the two other women – one of them a 'kulak' deported during total collectivisation, the other an elderly woman from Leningrad, wearing glasses with cracked lenses – wept beside her. Somehow it looked as if the cracks in the Leningrad woman's glasses had been made by her tears.

The guard did not know what to do. It was only very rarely that the *zeks* wept; their hearts were like the tundra – gripped by permanent frost.

The guard kept prodding the women in the back and begging, 'All right now, that's enough now, you shits . . . I'm asking you politely, you whores . . .'

He kept looking around for something. It never entered his head that the women might be weeping because of the music.

Nor did Masha herself understand why her heart was suddenly overflowing with anguish and despair. It was as if everything that had ever happened to her had melded together: her mother's love; beautiful poems; the check woollen dress that so suited her; Andryusha; the grubby face of the interrogator; dawn over the suddenly gleaming light blue sea at Kelasuri, not far from Sukhumi; little Yulenka's chatter; Semisotov; the old nuns; the furious quarrels of the dykes; her anguish because her brigade leader had begun looking very intently at her, narrowing her eyes, just as Semisotov had done. Why had this merry dance music made Masha sense so acutely her filthy undershirt, the sour smell of her jacket, her damp boots that were as heavy as irons? Why, all of a sudden, this question that had cut like a razor blade through her heart: Why, why had all this happened to her? Why this terrible cold, this moral degradation, this new submissiveness to her camp fate?

And hope, which until then had always oppressed her heart with its living weight, now died.

As she listened to this merry dance music, Masha's hope of seeing Yulia died. Yulia was lost forever in the great network of children's centres and orphanages; she was lost in the vastness of the Union of Soviet Socialist Republics. In student hostels and clubs young people were dancing to merry music like this . . . And Masha understood that her husband was no more; he had been shot, and she would never see him again.

And she was left without hope, entirely alone . . . Never would she see Yulia – neither today, nor in the future, when she was an old woman with grey hair.

Lord, Lord, have pity on her. Pity her, Lord. Have mercy upon her.

A year later Masha left the camp. Before returning to freedom, she lay for a while on some pine planks in a freezing hut. No one tried to hurry her out to work, and no one abused her. The medical orderlies placed Masha Lyubimova in a rectangular box made from boards that the timber inspectors had rejected for any other use. This was the last time anyone looked at her face. On it was a sweet, childish expression of delight and confusion, the same look as when she had stood by the timber store and listened to the merry music, first with joy and then with the realisation that all hope had vanished.

And Ivan Grigoryevich reflected that in the camps, in the labour camps of Kolyma, men were not equal to women. Men, really, had it easier.

14

In a dream Ivan Grigoryevich saw his mother. She was walking down a road, keeping to one side, out of the way of a long line of tractors and dump trucks. She did not see her son. He was shouting, 'Mama, Mama, Mama,' but the heavy roar of the tractors drowned out his voice.

He had no doubt that she would recognise him. For all the chaos on the road, she would see that this old greybeard from the camps was her son – if only she could hear him, if only she would look round. But she did not hear him; she did not look round.

He opened his eyes in despair. Bending over him was a woman, half dressed. He had called out to his mother in a dream, and this woman had come to him.

She was there beside him. He felt at once, with all his being, that she was beautiful. She had heard him cry out in his sleep and she had come to him, feeling tenderness and pity towards him. The woman's eyes were not weeping, but in them he could see something more important than tears of compassion. He saw something he had never before seen in the eyes of anyone.

She was beautiful because she was kind. He took her hand. She lay down beside him and he sensed her warmth, her tender breasts, her shoulders, her hair. It was as if he were sensing all this in his sleep; never, while awake, had he felt happy.

She was kindness, all kindness, and he understood with the whole of his corporal being that her tenderness, her warmth, her whispers were beautiful because her heart was full of kindness towards him, because love is kindness.

A first night of love . . .

'I don't want to remember it – it's too painful – but it's impossible to forget it. It's all still there. Asleep or not, it's still living. A piece of iron in my heart, like a shell fragment. Something you can never get away from. How could I forget? I was already grown up.

'Darling, I loved my husband very much. I was beautiful, but I wasn't a good person. I wasn't kind. I was twenty-two. You wouldn't have loved me then, even if I was beautiful. I know, I can feel it as a woman. I know I'm more to you than just this, than the two of us lying here together. As for me – don't be angry if I say I look on you as Christ. I keep wanting to confess – to repent before you, as if before God. My good one, my desired one, I want to tell you about it. I want to recall everything that happened.

'No, there was no famine at the time of the dispossession of the kulaks. All that happened then was that some of the land went out of cultivation, that's all. The famine began in 1932, well over a year after what we called "dekulakisation".

'I worked as a cleaner in the building of the district executive committee; I used to wash the floors. A friend of mine used to wash the floors in the land office. We heard a great deal. I can tell you everything, everything that happened. The old accountant used to tell me I should have been a government minister. It's true – I understand things quickly, and I've got a good memory.

'Dekulakisation began in late 1929, and the campaign was at its fiercest in February and March 1930.

First of all, before there were any arrests, the kulaks were asked to pay a special tax. They paid up; somehow they found the money. Then they were taxed a second time. Anything they could, they sold. They believed that if they paid up the State would be merciful. There were some, though, who made vodka out of their grain and slaughtered their cattle. They felt there was nothing left in their lives, so they just ate and drank.

'In other provinces things may have been different, but this is how it went in our province. At first it was only the heads of families who were arrested. Most of the men they took had fought for the Whites, in Denikin's Cossack units. This first wave of arrests was carried out by the OGPU; the Party activists played no part at all. And everyone arrested was shot – to the last man. Those arrested in late December, however, were kept in prison for two or three months and then sent to special settlements.* When it was a father who had been arrested, the rest of the family were left alone, except that an inventory was made of all their property; the family was no longer considered to own the property but merely to have been entrusted with it for safe keeping.

'The provincial Party committee would draw up a plan – that is, the total number of arrests to be made – and send it to each district Party committee. The district committees would then decide on the number of kulaks to be arrested in each village – and the village soviets would each draw up a list of names. It was on the basis of these lists that people were arrested. And who drew up the lists? A group of three – a troika. A group of three ordinary, muddle-headed people determined who was to live and who was to die. There were no holds barred. There were bribes . . . There were scores to be settled because of a woman, or because of some other past grievance . . . Often it was the poorest peasants who were listed as kulaks, while the richer peasants managed to buy themselves off.

'I can see now, though, that it's not simply a matter of

the lists having been drawn up by the wrong people. There were in any case more honest, sincere people among the activists than there were scoundrels. But the evil committed by the honest people was no less than the evil committed by the bad people. What matters is that the very existence of these lists was unjust and evil. Precisely who was included in them is hardly the point. Ivan was innocent – and Pyotr was no less innocent. Who was it that established the total figure, the number of arrests for the whole country? Who drew up the grand plan? Who signed it?

'The fathers were already in prison, and then, at the beginning of 1930, the authorities began to round up the families too. This was more than the OGPU could do on its own, and so the Party activists were mobilised too. The activists were just villagers like anyone else, they were people everyone knew, but they all seemed to lose their minds. They seemed dazed, crazed, as if they'd fallen under a spell. They threatened people with guns. They called small children "kulak brats". "You're Bloodsuckers!" they yelled, "Bloodsuckers!" And the "bloodsuckers" were white as sheets – they hardly had a drop of blood left in their veins. As for the activists, their eyes were like glass; they were like the eyes of cats. And yet, for the main part, they were people from our own village. They were, admittedly, under a spell. They'd convinced themselves that the kulaks were evil, that it was best not even to touch them. They would not even sit down to eat with one of "those parasites". The kulaks' towels were unclean, their children were disgusting, their young women were worse than lice. The activists looked on those who were being dispossessed as if they were cattle, or swine. Everything about the kulaks was vile – they were vile in themselves, and they had no souls, and they stank, and they were full of sexual diseases, and worst of all, they were enemies of the people and exploiters of the labour of others. The poor, the Komsomol and the police – they were all Chapaevs, every one of them a hero. In reality, though, you only had to look at these activists and it was obvious they were just people like any other people – some were green and inexperienced, and a fair number of them were plain scoundrels.

'All these words had their effect on me too. I was only a girl – and during meetings and special briefings, from films, books, articles and radio broadcasts, from Stalin himself, I was always hearing the same thing: that kulaks are parasites, that kulaks burn bread and murder children. The fury of the masses had to be ignited against them – yes, those were the words; it was proclaimed that the kulaks as a class must be destroyed, every accursed one of them . . . I too began to fall under this spell. It seemed that every misfortune was because of the kulaks; if we were to annihilate them immediately, then happy days would dawn for us all. No mercy was to be shown to the kulaks. They were not even human beings; goodness knows what they were – some kind of beasts, I suppose. And so I became an activist. And there were all sorts among us activists. There were those who truly believed, who hated the "parasites" and who really did do all they could for the poorest peasants; there were those with their own selfish aims; and then there were those – the majority – who were simply obeying orders, people willing to beat their own mothers and fathers to death if that was what they were told to do. The most terrible of all were not those who believed in the happy life that would begin once the kulaks were all done away with – no, the beasts that appear wildest are not always the most dangerous. The most terrible of all were the ones with selfish aims. They never stopped talking about political awareness – and all the time they were settling personal scores, stealing and plundering, destroying the lives of others. They destroyed others just to get hold of a few possessions, for a mere pair of boots. It was so easy to destroy: just write a denunciation – you don't even need to put your signature to it. Just say that your neighbour owned three cows, or that he had hired hands working for him – and there, you've set him up as a kulak. I saw what was happening and I was, of course, upset – but it didn't affect me deep down. It was the same as if farmyard cattle were being slaughtered in the wrong way – that too would have upset me – but I wouldn't have lost sleep over it.

'Don't you remember how you once answered a question of mine? Me – I shall never forget your words. Those words of yours opened my eyes; they brought me the light of day. I asked you how the Germans could send Jewish children to die in the gas chambers. How, I asked, could they live with themselves after that? Was there really no judgement passed on them by man or God? And you said: Only one judgement is passed on the executioner – he ceases to be a human being. Through looking on his victim as less than human, he becomes his own executioner; he executes the human being inside himself. But the victim – no matter what the executioner does to kill him – remains a human being forever. Remember now?

'I understand now why I chose to become a cook, why I didn't want to go on being the chairman of a collective farm. But I've told you about that already.

'When I look back now, I see the liquidation of the kulaks very differently. I'm no longer under a spell. I can see now that the kulaks were human beings. But why was my heart so frozen at the time? When such terrible things were being done, when such suffering was going on all around me? And the truth is that I truly didn't think of them as human beings. "They're not human beings, they're kulak trash!" – that's what I heard again and again, that's what everyone kept repeating. And when I think about it all now, I wonder who first talked about kulak trash. Lenin? Was it really Lenin?

How the kulaks suffered. In order to kill them, it was necessary to declare that kulaks are not human beings. Just as the Germans said that Yids are not human beings. That's what Lenin and Stalin said too: The kulaks are not human beings. But that's a lie. They are people. They are human beings. I can see now that we are all human beings.*

'And so, at the beginning of 1930 they began dispossessing the kulaks' families. The campaign was at its most frenzied in February and March. The district committee was hurrying everything on. They wanted every kulak out before the spring sowing. Then a new life would begin. We kept talking about our "first collective-farm spring".

'The activist committees, of course, were in charge of the expulsions. But they had been given no detailed instructions. Some collective-farm chairmen gathered together so many carts that no one knew what to do with them. The "grasping kulaks" didn't have enough possessions to fill them, so they went off in half-empty carts. The kulaks from our village, on the other hand, were sent out on foot. They took only what they could carry on their own backs – blankets and clothing. The mud was so deep it kept sucking their boots off their feet. It was a terrible sight. They walked on, a whole column of them, looking back all the time at their huts. They must have still been carrying inside them the warmth from their own stoves. Heaven knows what they were feeling. They had been born in those huts. It was from those huts that they had given their daughters away in marriage. Their stoves were still burning – they had had to leave cabbage soup that was only half cooked, milk that they hadn't had time to drink. There was smoke coming out of their chimneys. The women were weeping, but they were too scared to howl. And what did we care? We were – activists. We could just as well have been driving a flock of geese down the road. And on a cart following behind them were Pelageya the blind woman, old Dmitry Ivanovich who hadn't been out of his hut for ten years because of his legs, and Marusya the Fool, who had been kicked on the temple by a horse when she was still a child and who had been in a daze ever since.

'And in the district centre there was no room in the prison. You couldn't really call it a prison at all – just a lock-up. And there were whole armies of kulaks – a column from every village. The cinema, the theatre, the clubs and schools – all of them were turned into prisons. But people weren't kept there for long. Soon they were taken to the station, where trains of empty goods wagons were waiting in the sidings. They were taken there under guard – grandfathers and grandmothers, women and children, all escorted by the police and the OGPU as if they were murderers. There were no fathers – the fathers, remember, had all been arrested a few months before. People whispered, "There go the kulaks." It was as if they were talking about wolves. Some even shouted out curses at them – but the prisoners were no longer weeping, their faces were like stone . . .

'I didn't see them being taken away in trains myself, but other people have told me what happened. Later, trying to escape the famine, there were fellow villagers who managed to join the kulaks in their settlements beyond the Urals. And a close friend sent me a letter. And there were people who escaped from their special settlements. I talked to two of them myself.

'They were transported in sealed goods wagons. Their belongings went separately. All they could take with them was the food they had in their hands. And at one station the fathers were all put on the train. That day there was great joy in the goods wagons, and great tears. The journey lasted more than a month – peasants were being taken from all over Russia and the railway lines were jammed with transport trains.

There were no bed boards in the cattle wagons. Everyone just slept on the floor, packed together. The sick, of course, died before they reached their destination. But still, people did at least get fed. At each of the main stations there were pails of gruel, and two hundred grams of bread per head.

'The guards were ordinary soldiers, not OGPU. They weren't vicious – they simply treated the peasants like they were cattle. So my friend wrote in her letter.

'And I've heard what it was like when they finally got there, I heard from those who escaped. Everyone was simply scattered about the taiga. If you were old or sick, if you couldn't work, you were dropped off in a village in the forest. The village huts ended up as crowded as the cattle wagons had been. And everyone else was just set down in the middle of nowhere; they were left to fend for themselves in the snow. The weak froze to death. Those who were able to work began cutting down trees. They left the stumps where they were, pulled the trunks along the ground and began building makeshift shelters. They worked without a break, almost without sleeping, so that their families wouldn't freeze to death. Only later did they have time to build proper log huts – two-room huts, one family in each room. They built those huts on no foundation but moss, and they filled in the gaps between the logs with more moss.

'Those who were fit for work were bought from the OGPU by State logging enterprises. The logging enterprises supplied them with all they needed for work, and with rations for their dependants. The huts they'd built were called a "labour settlement", and everything was supervised by a "command-ant" and by "foremen". They were paid, apparently, the same as local workers, though all their pay went into special books.* Our people are strong, and soon they began to earn more than the locals. But they had to stay within bounds – either in the settlement itself or in the logging area. Later on, during the War, they were allowed to travel within the region. And after the War heroes of labour could go outside the region. Some even received internal passports.

'As for those considered unfit for work, my friend said that they were formed into "labour colonies". These were supposed to be self-sufficient – they were just loaned some seed and supplied with rations to keep people going until the first harvest. Otherwise the "colonies" were much the same as the settlements – supervised by guards and a commandant. Later they were turned into cooperatives. There was still a commandant, but the peasants also had their own representatives.

'Meanwhile, back in the village, our new life began. Now that there were no more "kulaks", everyone was forced to join the collective farm. There were meetings that lasted all night long – with endless cursing and shouting. Some people were refusing to join; others said that they didn't mind joining but that they weren't going to give up their cows. Then came Stalin's article in *Pravda*, "Dizziness from Success".* Once again there was chaos. "But you can't force us to join," people protested. "Stalin says so himself." People began writing declarations on scraps of newspaper, "I am leaving the collective to become an independent farmer." But after a while the authorities began forcing everyone to rejoin the collectives. As for the property left by the kulaks, most of it simply got stolen.

'And we all thought that no fate could be worse than that of the kulaks. How wrong we were. In the villages the axe fell on everyone – no one was big enough, or small enough, to be safe.

'This time it was execution by hunger.

'By then I was a bookkeeper; I had moved on from washing floors. As an activist, I was sent to the Ukraine to "reinforce" a collective farm. The spirit of private property, we were told,

132

was more powerful there than in Russia. That's as may be – but it's certainly true that they were having a hard time of it, even harder than we were. I wasn't sent far. Our own village was right on the border with the Ukraine, and this collective farm was less than three hours away. It was a beautiful place. And the people there were like people anywhere else. And so I became their bookkeeper.

'I think I learned about everything that went on there. It's really not for nothing that the old accountant said I should have been a government minister. I only say this because I'm telling you everything – I'm not in the habit of boasting. I could have kept all the accounts without even using paper – it was all there in my head. And when we had training sessions, when our troika held meetings or our bosses got drunk, I took in everything that was said.

'How did it all happen? After the dispossession of the kulaks, the area of land under cultivation dropped sharply, and so did the crop yield. But everyone kept reporting that, without the kulaks, our life had immediately started to blossom. The village soviet lied to the district, the district to the province, and the province to Moscow. Everyone wanted Stalin to rejoice in the belief that a happy life had begun and the whole of his dominion would soon be awash with collective-farm grain. The time came for the first collective-farm harvest. Everything seemed in order. Moscow determined the quotas for grain deliveries from each province, and the provinces determined the quota for each district. And our village was given a quota it couldn't have fulfilled in ten years. All the members of the village soviet were terrified; even the tee-totallers took to drink. It was clear that Moscow had put all its hopes on the Ukraine. And so it was the Ukraine, above all, that then got the blame. Everyone understood very well: if you fail to fulfil the plan, you're a kulak yourself – and you should have been liquidated long ago.

'It was, of course, impossible to fulfil the plan. The area under cultivation was down, and so were yields. Where was it then – this ocean of collective-farm grain? It must have been hidden away! Idlers, parasites, kulaks who had not yet been liquidated! The kulaks had been deported, but their spirit endured. The Ukrainian peasant was in thrall to private property.

'Who signed the decree? Who ordered the mass murder? Was it really Stalin? I often ask myself. Never, I believe, in all Russian history, has there been such a decree. No Tsar, nor even the Tatars or German Fascists, ever signed such a decree. The decree meant the death by famine of the peasants of the Ukraine, the Don and the Kuban. It meant the death of them and their children. Even their entire seed fund was to be confiscated. The authorities searched for that grain as if they were searching for bombs and machine guns. They stabbed the earth with bayonets and ramrods; they smashed floors and dug underneath them; they dug up vegetable gardens.* Sometimes they requisitioned the grain inside people's huts, the grain people had put in pots and tubs. One woman had some bread requisitioned, loaves that had already been baked. It too was loaded onto the cart and taken off to the district centre.

'Day and night the carts creaked along, clouds of dust hung over the earth – but there were no silos to store all this grain in. The grain was simply dumped on the ground, with sentries standing guard all around it. By the beginning of winter the grain was soaking and beginning to rot. The Soviet authorities did not have enough tarpaulins to protect the peasants' grain.

'And while they were still transporting the grain, there was dust wherever you went. It was like clouds of smoke – over the village, over the fields, over the face of the moon at night. I remember one man going out of his mind. "We're on fire!" he

134

kept screaming. "The sky is burning! The earth is burning!" No, it was not the sky – it was life itself that was burning.

'That was when I understood: what mattered to the Soviet authorities was the plan. Fulfil the plan! Deliver your assigned quota of grain. The State is everything, and people are nothing.

'Mothers and fathers wanted to save their children, to put just a little grain to one side. They were told, "You hate the motherland of socialism with a ferocious hatred. You want to sabotage the plan. You're nothing but vermin, you subkulak parasites."* But they didn't want to sabotage the plan – they wanted to save their children, to save themselves. Everyone, after all, needs to eat.

'I can tell you the story, but a story is only words – and this was a matter of life and death, of torment, of people dying from starvation. When the grain was requisitioned, by the way, the Party activists were told that the peasants would be fed by the State. That was a lie. Not a single grain was given to the hungry.

'Who confiscated the grain? Mainly, it was local people: from the district executive committee and from the district Party committee; young lads from the Komsomol, locals all of them; the police, of course; and the OGPU. In a few places they even used army units. I only saw one man from Moscow. He'd been mobilised to the Ukraine by the Party, but he didn't seem very eager. He kept trying to go back home . . . Once again, though, the same as during collect-ivisation, people became dazed, crazed, like wild beasts.

'Grisha Saenko was a policeman. He was married to a local girl, and on holidays he used to come to the village and go to parties. He was bright and lively. He could dance the tango and the waltz, and he knew all the songs from the Ukrainian villages. One day an old man, a real greybeard, went up to him and said, "Grisha, you're ruining all of us.

What you're doing is worse than murder. Why does a workers' and peasants' state treat the peasantry worse than the Tsars did?" Grisha gave the old man a shove and then went off to the well to wash, saying, "How can I pick up a spoon with a hand that's just touched that vile parasite?"

'And the dust. Day and night, while they were confiscating the grain, there was dust. And at night the moon hung there like a stone, taking up half the sky. And everything beneath that moon seemed strange and wild. And it was so hot at night – like under a sheepskin. And fields that had been trampled, trampled and trampled again . . . Just to set eyes on them was like reading a death sentence.

'People began to lose their minds. The cattle kept lowing plaintively – they were becoming timid, frightened of people. The dogs howled all night. And the earth began to crack from the heat.

'Then came autumn, and autumn rains. And then a snowy winter. And there was no bread.

'There was no bread for sale in the district centre – it was only for those who had ration cards. Nor could you buy it at a railway station kiosk – there were armed guards who didn't let you anywhere near the station without special permission. You couldn't buy bread anywhere, at any price.

'During the autumn people took to living on potatoes – but without bread, it doesn't take long to get through potatoes. Towards Christmas they began slaughtering their cattle – but the cattle were nothing, just skin and bones. They slaughtered the chickens, of course. Soon they'd got through all their meat. And there wasn't so much as a drop of milk to be found in the village. Nor was there a single egg. And worst of all, there was no grain, no bread. Every last kernel had been requisitioned. Come spring, there would be no spring wheat to sow, the entire seed fund had gone. People's only hope was the winter wheat, but that was still under the snow. There was no sign of spring, and the village was already beginning to starve. They'd eaten all the meat. They'd eaten what millet they had. They were getting to the end of their stock of potatoes – the larger families already had none left at all.

'People began begging for loans of grain. From the village soviet, from the district committee. They didn't get a word in answer. And it was nineteen kilometres to the district centre, and there were no horses.

'It was terrible. Mothers looked at their own children – and screamed in fear. It was as if they'd seen a snake in the house. And they had seen a snake; they had seen famine, starvation, death. What could they do? No one in the village could think of anything except food. People would suck and move their jaws up and down. The saliva would flow, and they'd swallow it down – but you need more than saliva to fill up your stomach. If you woke in the night there wasn't a sound to be heard. No one talking anywhere, no one playing an accordion. The silence of the grave. No footsteps but the footsteps of famine – famine never slept. First thing in the morning, the children in every hut were crying, asking for bread. And what were their mothers to give them? Snow? There was no help to be had from anyone. The Party officials just went on repeating, "You shouldn't have lazed about like that. You should have worked harder." Sometimes they added, "Just look around you. There's enough grain been buried here for the next three years!"

'Still, there was no real famine that winter. People became weak, of course. Their stomachs began to bulge from eating just scraps and peelings, but there was no real dropsy. They began digging up acorns from under the snow. They dried them; the miller set his stones further apart – and he ground them up into flour. People began making bread – flatbreads, really – from acorns. Some people added bran, or ground-up potato peelings. But the acorns didn't last long – it was only a small oak wood and three whole villages had descended on it at once. Meanwhile, a Party official came from the city and said to us in the village soviet, "See what those parasites are like! Digging for acorns! Digging under the snow with their bare hands! Anything to get out of work!"

'The senior classes carried on going to school almost until it was spring, but the junior classes stopped during the winter. And in spring the school closed and the teacher went off to the city. The medical assistant left too; there was nothing for him to eat. And there are no medicines against hunger. The village was left to look after itself – with everyone starving in their huts, and nothing but desert on all sides. And the various officials from the city stopped visiting. There was nothing more to be taken from the starving people – so why should anyone go to the village? There was nothing a teacher could teach them – and nothing a medical assistant could do. Once the State's squeezed all it can out of you, then you're no more use to it. No point in teaching or healing you.

'The villagers were abandoned; the State withdrew from them. People began wandering from house to house, begging from one another. Poor begged from poor; the starving from the starving. Those with large families begged from those with small families, and from those who had no children at all. Some people still had a little left at the beginning of spring, and they would give away a handful of bran or a couple of potatoes. But the Party members never gave anyone anything at all – not because they were especially greedy, or especially bad, but simply because they were frightened. And the State didn't give the starving so much as one grain of wheat – even though the grain grown by the peasants was its very foundation. Did Stalin know all this? The old people talked about the famine at the time of the Tsar. Then there had been help. They had been given loans. The peasants had gone to the cities; they'd begged for alms "in the name of Christ". Soup kitchens had been opened, and students had collected donations. But under a workers' and peasants' government no one had given them a single grain. And there were roadblocks – manned by soldiers, police and OGPU – on every road. The starving had to stay in their villages – they were not to walk to the cities. There were guards around every railway station, even around the smallest halts. For those who fed the nation there was no bread. And in the cities the workers were receiving eight hundred grams of bread a day on their ration cards. Eight hundred grams! Good God, it was unimaginable. And not a gram for the peasant children in the villages. It was the same as the Nazis putting Jewish children in the gas chambers: "You're Yids – you've no right to live." But what we did was beyond all understanding: it was the Soviet people against the Soviet people, Russians against Russians, and a government of workers and peasants. So why all this killing?

'It was when the snow began to melt that the real hunger began.

'The children were crying. They no longer slept; they were asking for bread even at night. People's faces were ashen; their eyes were clouded, as if drunk. They walked about as if half asleep, resting one hand against the wall and moving one foot at a time, testing the ground with it. Hunger makes people unsteady. People began to move about less and to spend more and more time lying down. And they kept imagining they could hear the sound of a cart: flour, sent by Stalin from the district centre, to save their children.

'The women turned out to be stronger, more stubborn, than the men; they clung to life more fiercely. But they also had more to endure – it's their mothers, after all, whom children turn to for food. Some women tried to reason with their children. They would kiss them and say, "Don't cry. Be patient. There just isn't anything." Others went almost out of their minds. "Stop that whining," they'd shout, "or I'll kill you!" And they'd lay into their children with whatever was at hand – anything to stop their pleading. Some escaped from their houses and sat with their neighbours so as not to hear their children crying.

'By this time there were no dogs or cats left. They had all been slaughtered. Not that it had been easy to catch them. They were afraid of people by then, and they looked at them with wild eyes. People boiled the animals, but there was nothing except dry tendons. They made a kind of meat jelly out of their heads.

'So the snow melted and people began to swell. It was the dropsy of starvation. They had swollen faces and legs like pillows. Their stomachs were full of water and they were constantly peeing. They kept having to go outside. As for the children – did you see the newspaper photographs of children from the German camps? They looked just the same: heads heavy as cannonballs; thin little necks, like the necks of storks; and you could see every little bone in their arms and legs. Every single little bone moving under their skin, and the joints between them. And draped over their skeletons was a kind of yellow gauze. And the children's faces looked old and tormented – it was as if they'd been on this earth for seventy years. By the spring they no longer had faces at all. Some had the heads of birds, with a little beak; some had the heads of frogs, with thin wide lips; some looked like little gudgeons, with wide-open mouths. Non-human faces. And their eyes! Dear God! Comrade Stalin, by God, did you see those eyes? Perhaps he truly did not know. It was he, after all, who wrote that article, the one about dizziness from success.

'There was nothing people didn't eat. They caught mice;

they caught rats, jackdaws, sparrows and ants; they dug up earthworms. They ground up old bones to make flour. They cut up leather, the soles of shoes, stinking old animal hides to make something like noodles; then they boiled the noodles up to make a kind of gummy paste. When plants and grasses began to sprout, they dug up roots and boiled leaves and buds. There was nothing they didn't use: dandelions, burdock, bluebells, willowherb, goutweed, hogweed, nettles, stonecrop . . . They dried linden leaves and ground them into flour, but we only had a few lindens. The flatbreads made from linden leaves were green, worse than the ones made from acorns.

'And still no help. Not that anyone was asking for it any longer. Even now, when I start to think of it all, I feel I'm losing my mind. Did Stalin really turn his back on all these people? Did he really carry out such a massacre? Stalin had food; Stalin had bread. It seems that he chose to kill all these people, that he starved them deliberately. They didn't even help the children. So was Stalin worse than Herod? Did he take away people's last kernels of grain – and then starve them? "No," I say to myself, "how could he?" But then I say to myself, "It happened, it happened." And then, immediately: "No, it couldn't have!"

'While they still had a little strength, people used to walk through the fields to the railway. Not to the station – no, the guards didn't let them anywhere near it – but just to the track itself. When the Kiev–Odessa express came by, they used to kneel down and shout, "Bread! Bread!" Sometimes they held their children up in the air – their terrible children. And sometimes people would throw them pieces of bread or some scraps. The dust would settle, the rumble of the train would pass – and the whole village would be crawling along the track, searching for crusts. But then came new regulations; when trains were passing through the famine provinces, the OGPU guards had to close the windows and lower the blinds. Passengers weren't allowed to look out. And the peasants had stopped going to the railway anyway. They no longer had the strength to go outside their huts, let alone as far as the railway.

'I remember how one old man showed the farm chairman a scrap of newspaper he'd picked up by the railway. There was an item about a Frenchman, a famous minister, who'd come to the Soviet Union. He was taken to Dnepropetrovsk Province, where the famine was at its most terrible, even worse than where we were. People were eating people there. He was taken to a village, to a collective-farm nursery school, and he asked the children what they'd had for lunch that day. "Chicken soup with pies and rice croquettes," came the answer. I saw those words with my own eyes, I can see that piece of newspaper even now. There's never been anything like it. Killing millions on the quiet and then duping the whole world. Chicken soup! Rice croquettes! Where we were, every last worm had been eaten. And the old man went on, "Under Tsar Nicholas our newspapers told the whole world about the famine. 'Help us, help us!' they wrote. 'Our peasants are dying.' But you monsters, you Herods – you just turn it all into one big show!"*

'From the village came a howl; it had seen its own death. The whole village was howling, without mind, without heart. It was a noise like leaves in the wind, or creaking straw. It made me angry. Why did they have to howl so pitifully? They had ceased to be human – so why were they crying so pitifully? You'd have to be made of stone to carry on eating your bread ration to the sound of that howling. I used to go out into the fields with my bread ration; I'd stop – and I could still hear them howling. I'd go a bit further – and it would seem they'd gone silent. Then I'd go further still – and I could hear it again. Only by then it was from the next village. It would seem as if, along with the people, the whole earth had begun to howl. "Who's going to hear them?" I'd think. "There's no God."

'An OGPU officer once said to me, "You know what your villages are called by people at provincial headquarters? Cemeteries of a severe school!" But at first I didn't understand what he meant. And the weather was wonderful. We had quick, light showers early that summer, alternating with a hot sun. The wheat stood thick as a wall, taller than a man – as if you'd need an axe in order to cut it! I saw any number of rainbows that summer, and thunderstorms, and warm "gypsy" rain, as they call it.

'All winter long everyone had been wondering about the harvest, searching for omens and questioning the old men. The winter wheat had been their only hope. And it proved everything they'd hoped for – but they were too weak to harvest it. I went into one hut. Everyone was lying down, barely breathing, or maybe not breathing at all, it was hard to tell. Some were on beds, some on the stove.* The daughter – a girl I knew – was lying on the floor in a kind of madness, gnawing the leg of a stool. And what was worst of all is that she just growled when I came in. She didn't look round when she heard me. She just growled, the way a dog growls if you go too close when he's gnawing a bone.

'The whole village died.* First it was the children, then it was the old people, then it was the middle-aged. In the beginning people dug graves for them, but then they stopped. And so the dead were lying on the streets, in the yards, and the last to die just remained in their huts. It went quiet. The whole village had died. Who was the last to die, I don't know. Those of us who worked in the administration were taken off to the town.

'I ended up in Kiev. This was the time when bread came back on sale again. Even without a ration card, it became possible to buy bread. You should have seen it. People began queuing the evening before – and even then the queues were half a mile long. There are many kinds of queues, you know: queues where people make jokes and crunch sunflower seeds; queues where your number is written down on a piece of paper; and queues where no one is joking and your number is written on the palm of your hand or chalked on your back.* But these queues weren't like any of these; no, I've never seen anything like them. People put their arms around the waist of the person in front and clung up against them. If anyone stumbled the whole queue would sway; it was as if a wave had passed through it. And a kind of dance would begin, people swaying from side to side. The swaying would get wilder and wilder. People were afraid they wouldn't have the strength to keep hold of the person in front, that they'd lose their grip – and this fear would make the women start howling, and soon the whole queue would be screaming and it was as if they'd all gone out of their minds, as if they were singing and dancing. Sometimes young louts would try to break into the queue; you could see them looking for the weakest link. When these louts came close, everyone would be howling with fear again – and again, it was as if they were singing. All this was just townsfolk without ration cards queuing to buy bread – people without passports, people stripped of their civic rights,* ordinary artisans or people who lived out in the suburbs.

'And then there were the peasants – crawling out of their villages, crawling towards the city. The stations were all cordoned off, and the trains were constantly searched. There were army and OGPU roadblocks on every road. All the same, people were getting to Kiev, crawling through fields and bogs, through woods and open country – anything to bypass the roadblocks. It was impossible, after all, to set up blocks everywhere. The peasants could no longer walk – they could only crawl. And so people in Kiev would be hurrying about their affairs – on their way to work, on their way to a cinema . . . Trams would be running . . . And in the middle of all this, crawling about among these people, were the starving. Children, men, young girls – all on all fours. They looked more like some kind of filthy little cats or dogs. But they seemed to be trying to be like people. They knew modesty; they knew shame. You'd see a young girl crawling along – all swollen, whining, looking like some kind of monkey. And then she'd be putting her skirt straight, tucking her long hair under her kerchief. She was, after all, from a village, and this was her first time in Kiev. But it was only the lucky few, only one in ten thousand, who managed to crawl as far as Kiev. Not that it helped them – there was no salvation even in Kiev. Starving people lay on the ground. They begged, they tried to hiss out words – but they were unable to eat. Someone might have a crust of bread beside him but he couldn't see it any more; he was too far gone.

'Every morning horses pulled flat-top carts through the city. Those who'd died in the night were taken away. I saw one cart, it was stacked with the bodies of children. It was like I've already said. They looked thin and long – faces like dead birdies, sharp little beaks. These little birds had flown to Kiev – and what good had it done them? Some were still making cheeping noises; their little heads were like ripe ears of grain, bending the thin stalks of their necks. I asked the driver. He just shrugged his shoulders. "They'll quieten down soon enough," he said.

'I saw one young girl crawl across the pavement. A street sweeper gave her a kick, and she rolled onto the roadway. She didn't look round. She just crawled on, fast as she could, heaven knows where she got the strength from. And she even tried to shake the dust off her dress. That same day I bought a Moscow paper. I read an article by Maksim Gorky about how children need *educational toys*. Did Gorky not know about the children stacked on the cart? Did they really need *educational toys*? Or maybe Gorky did know – and kept silent, like everyone kept silent. And maybe he too wrote that those dead children were enjoying chicken soup. That same driver told me that the greatest number of dead was by the shops that sold unrationed bread. If you're starving, if you're swollen with dropsy, a single crust can finish you off. Yes, I remember Kiev all right, even though I only spent three days there.

'And this is what I came to understand. At first, hunger drives you out of your home. In the beginning, it burns and torments you – it tears at your guts, at your soul. And so you try to escape your home. People dig for worms, they gather grass – and yes, they even try to fight their way through to Kiev. Whatever they do, they've got to get out, they've got to get away. And then the day comes when the starving man crawls back into his home. That means hunger has won. This one has given up the struggle; he lies down on his bed and stays there. And once hunger has won, you can't get the man up again, try as you might. Not just because he doesn't have the strength but because it's all the same to him; he no longer wants to go on living. He just lies there quietly. All he wants is to be left alone. He doesn't want to eat, he can't stop peeing, he has the runs. All he wants is to sleep, to be left in peace. If you just lie there quietly, it means you're near the end. I've heard the same from prisoners of war. If a prisoner just lay there on the boards, if he stopped caring about his rations, that meant he was close to dying. But there were some people who lost their minds. They only went still at the very end. You could recognise them by their bright, shining eyes. These were the ones who cut up corpses and boiled them, who even killed and ate their own children. As the human being in them died, the wild beast came to the surface. I saw one woman who'd been brought to the district centre under guard. She had a human face but the eyes of a wolf. Cannibals, I've heard, were all shot, every last one of them. But these cannibals were not guilty. The guilty ones were those who drove a mother to eat her own children. But you can look all you like – you won't find anyone who admits to being guilty. What they did, they did for the good of everyone. That's why they drove mothers to eat their own children.

'I understood then that every starving man is a kind of cannibal. He eats the flesh off his own body. He leaves only the bones. He consumes his last droplet of fat. Then his mind goes dark – he has eaten his own brains. The starving man has eaten himself up.

'I also realised that every starving man dies in his own way. In one hut they're at war, checking on one another, keeping watch on one another, stealing crumbs from one another. Wife against husband; husband against wife. The mother hates her children. But in another hut they live in indestructible love. I knew one woman with four children. She could hardly move her tongue, but she kept telling them fairy tales to try to make them forget their hunger. She hardly had the strength even to lift her own arms, yet she held her children in them. Love lived on in her. Where there was hate, it seemed people died more quickly. But love, for that matter, did not save anyone. Every last person lay down and died. There was no life left.

'The village, I learned later, went silent. There was no sound of children. There was no longer any need for educational toys – or for chicken soup. There was no wailing – no one left to wail. I learned later that troops were sent in to harvest the winter wheat – but they weren't allowed to enter the dead village. They camped in their tents. They were told that there'd been an epidemic. They kept complaining, though, about the terrible smell from the village. The troops also sowed winter wheat for the following year. And in the spring settlers were brought in from Oryol Province. This was, after all, the Ukraine. It was Black Earth – and Oryol has always been a land of bad harvests. The women and children were left in shelters by the station, and the men were taken into the village. They were given pitchforks and told to go round the huts and drag out the bodies. The dead were just lying there, men and women, some on beds and some on the floor. The smell in the huts was awful. The men tied kerchiefs over their mouths and noses and began dragging out the bodies – but the bodies just fell apart. Finally, all the bits of bodies were buried outside the village. That's when I understood that the village truly was a "cemetery of a severe school". Once all the corpses were gone, they brought in the women to clean the floors and whitewash the walls. Everything was done properly, but the smell was still there. They whitewashed the walls a second time and spread new clay on the floors, but the smell still wouldn't go away. They couldn't eat in those huts, and they couldn't sleep in those huts; they all went back to Oryol. But still, earth like that doesn't stay empty and unpeopled for long. How could it?

'And now it's as if those people never lived. But the village had seen all kinds of things. There had been love. Wives leaving husbands, and daughters getting married. People had had drunken fights, and they had had friends and family to stay. They had baked bread. And how they had worked! They had sung songs. Their children had gone to school. Sometimes the mobile cinema had come, and everyone – even the old folks – had gone to see a film.

'And nothing remains of all that. Where can that life have gone? And that suffering, that terrible suffering? Can there really be nothing left? Is it really true that no one will be held to account for it all? That it will all just be forgotten without a trace?

'Grass has grown over it.

'How can this be? – I ask you.

'Look – it's getting light. Our night's over now. It's time we both got ready to go out to work.'

15

Vasily Timofeyevich had a quiet voice and a hesitant way of moving. As for Ganna, when someone spoke to her, she would look down at the ground with her brown eyes and reply almost inaudibly.

After their marriage, they both became still more timid. He was fifty years old, and the neighbours' children called him 'Grandad'; he was grey-haired, balding and wrinkled – and he felt embarrassed to have married someone so young. He felt ashamed to be so happy in his love, to find himself whispering, 'My darling, my sweetheart' as he looked at his wife. As for her, when she was a little girl, she had tried to imagine her future husband. He would be a Civil War hero like Shchors; he would be the best accordion player in the village; and he would be a writer of heartfelt poems like Taras Shevchenko. Nevertheless, even though Vasily Timofeyevich was no longer young, even though he was poor, timid and generally unlucky, even though he had always lived through others rather than living a life of his own, her meek heart understood the strength of the love he felt for her. And he understood how she, so young, had hoped for more, how she had dreamed of a village knight who would ride up and bear her away from her stepfather's cramped hut – instead of which he had come along in his old boots, with his big brown peasant hands, coughing apologetically and clearing his throat. And now here he was, looking at her happily, adoringly, guiltily and with grief. And she, for her part, felt guilty before him and was meek and silent.

They had a son, Grisha, a quiet little baby who never cried. His mother, now once again looking like a skinny little girl, sometimes went up to his cradle at night. Seeing the boy lying there with open eyes, she would say to him, 'Try crying a bit, little Grishenka. Why are you always so silent?'

Even when they were in their own hut both husband and wife always talked in soft voices. 'Why do you always speak so quietly?' neighbours would ask in astonishment.

It was strange that the young woman and her plain, elderly husband should be so alike, equally timid, equally meek in their hearts.

They both worked without a word of complaint. They did not even dare let out a sigh when the brigade leader was unjust, when he sent them out into the fields even if it was not their turn.

Once, Vasily Timofeyevich was sent to the district centre on an errand for the collective-farm stables; he went with the farm chairman. While the chairman was going about his business in the land and finance offices, he tied the horses to a post, went into the shop and bought his wife a treat: some poppy-seed cakes, some sweets, some bread rings,* some nuts. Not a lot, just 150 grams of each. When he got back home and untied his white kerchief, his wife flung her hands up in the air with joy and cried out, 'Oh! Mama!' In his embarrassment, Vasily Timofeyevich went off into the storeroom so that she would not see the tears of happiness in his eyes.

For Christmas she embroidered a shirt for her husband. Never did she learn that, after she had given it to him, Vasily Timofeyevich Karpenko was hardly able to sleep. Throughout the night he kept getting up and walking across, in his bare feet, to the little chest of drawers on top of which he had put the shirt. He kept stroking it with the palm of his hand, feeling the simple cross-stitch design . . . And when he was taking his wife home from the maternity ward of the district hospital, when he saw her holding their child in her arms, he felt that he would never forget this day – even if he were to live a thousand years.

Sometimes he felt frightened. How was it possible for such happiness to have come into his life? How was it possible that he could wake in the middle of the night and find himself listening to the breathing of a wife and a son?

Whoever he was with, Vasily Timofeyevich felt shy and timid. How could he have the right to something like this?

But that was how it was. He walked back from work and saw smoke coming out of the chimney and a baby's nappy drying on the fence. He would see his wife bending over the cradle or smiling about something as she put a bowl of borsch on the table. He would look at her hands, at her hair peeping out from beneath her kerchief. He would listen to her talking about their little one or about the neighbour's ewe. Sometimes she would go out into the storeroom and he would miss her and even feel lonely. As soon as she came back, he would feel happy again. Catching his eye, she would give him a sad, meek smile.

Vasily Timofeyevich died first, two days before little Grisha. He had been giving almost every crumb to his wife and child, and so he died before them. Probably there has been no self-sacrifice in the world greater than this – and no despair greater than his despair as he looked at his wife, already disfigured by the dropsy of death, and at his dying son.

Even during his last hour he felt no indignation, no anger with regard to the great and senseless thing accomplished by the State and Stalin. He did not even ask, 'Why?' He did not once ask why the torment of death by starvation had been allotted to him and his wife – meek, obedient and hard-working as they were – and to their quiet little one-year-old boy.

Still in their rotten rags, the skeletons spent the winter together. The husband, his young wife and their little son went on smiling whitely, not separated even by death.

The next spring, after the first starlings had arrived, the representative from the district land office entered the hut, covering his mouth and nose with a handkerchief. He looked at the paraffin lamp with no glass, at the icon in the corner, at the little chest of drawers, at the cold cast-iron pots and at the bed.

'Two and a child,' he called out.

The brigade leader, standing on this most holy threshold of love and meekness, nodded and made a mark on a scrap of paper.

Back in the fresh air, the representative looked at the white huts and the green orchards and said, 'Take the corpses away – but don't bother about this ruin. It's not worth trying to repair it.'

Once again the brigade leader nodded.

16

At work Ivan Grigoryevich learned that the officials in the municipal court accept bribes; that it's possible to buy good marks for young people sitting the entrance exams for the radio technical college; that a factory director will, for a bribe, supply cooperatives producing consumer goods with metals that are otherwise almost unobtainable; that, with the money he had stolen, the director of a mill had built himself a two-storey house and had had the floors laid with oak parquet; that the chief of police had released a notorious wheeler-dealer of a jeweller after his family had paid him the unbelievable sum of 600,000 roubles; and that the first secretary himself – the town boss – was willing, if properly compensated, to order the chairman of the town soviet to sign certificates entitling you to an apartment in a new building on the main street.

All morning Ivan Grigoryevich's fellow workers had been talking excitedly. They had just heard some important news from the provincial capital; a verdict had finally been reached in the case against the stock-keeper of the town's biggest cooperative, a manufacturer of fur coats, ladies' winter coats and reindeer and astrakhan fur hats. Although the principal defendant was only a humble stockroom boss, the case had taken on spectacular dimensions; like some giant octopus, it had wound its tentacles around the entire life of the city. The verdict had been impatiently awaited for a long time, and there had been many arguments about it during lunch breaks. Some thought that the investigator for especially important cases, who was from Moscow, would fearlessly expose every one of the town's most senior officials.

After all, even little children knew that the town prosecutor drove about in a Volga given to him by that balding stammerer of a stockroom boss; that the Party secretary now had new bedroom and dining-room suites that had come all the way from Riga; that the wife of the chief of police had gone to the Black Sea coast, by plane, to stay for two months – at the expense of this same stockroom boss – in the Council of Ministers' Sanatorium in Adler; and that before she left for the airport she had been given an emerald ring.

The more sceptical insisted that the Muscovite would never dare bring charges against the town officials and that the stockroom boss and the cooperative administration would have to answer for everything themselves.

And then the student son of the stockroom boss had flown in from the provincial capital with the unexpected news that the investigator for especially important cases had quashed the entire case for lack of evidence. The stockroom boss had been released from custody and the chairman and two other members of the cooperative administration had had their bail conditions lifted and were now free to travel.

For some reason the decision taken by the high-ranking Moscow investigator brought great merriment to the metal workshop. During the lunch break everyone, sceptics and optimists alike, joked and laughed as they ate their bread, sausage, tomatoes and cucumbers – and there was no knowing whether they were more amused by the human weakness of the investigator for especially important cases or by the apparent omnipotence of the balding stammerer of a stockroom boss.

And it occurred to Ivan Grigoryevich that it was perhaps

not so very surprising that incorruptible asceticism, the faith of the barefoot and fanatical apostles of the commune, had led in the end to fraudsters who were ready to do anything for the sake of a good dacha, for a car of their own, for some roubles to put away in their piggy bank.

After work one evening, Ivan Grigoryevich went to the polyclinic and knocked at the door of the doctor he had heard Anna Sergeyevna mention. The doctor, who had just finished seeing patients, was taking off his white coat.

'I would like to know, Doctor, about the health of Mikhalyova, Anna Sergeyevna.'

'Who are you?' asked the doctor. 'Are you her husband or father?'

'I'm not a relative, but she is someone very close to me.'

'I see,' said the doctor. 'Well, let me say then that she has lung cancer. There's nothing we can do. Neither a surgeon nor a sanatorium can help.'

17

Three weeks passed and Anna Sergeyevna went into hospital. As they said goodbye, she said to Ivan Grigoryevich, 'Happiness doesn't seem to be our fate in this world.'

In the afternoon, while Ivan Grigoryevich was out at work, Anna Sergeyevna's sister came and took Alyosha away, to live with her in her village.

Ivan Grigoryevich came back to an empty room. It was very quiet there. Although he had lived his whole life alone, it seemed that he had never before felt the full weight of loneliness.

That night he did not sleep; he was thinking. '. . . doesn't seem to be our fate in this world . . .' The only light seemed to be in his distant childhood.

Now that happiness had looked him in the eye, now that he had felt its breath on his face, he examined with great acuteness the life which had been his.

It was painful indeed to realise that he was powerless to save Anna Sergeyevna, that he could do nothing to ease the final sufferings that had already begun for her. Strangely, he seemed to find solace for his grief in thinking about the decades he had spent in camps and prisons.

He was trying to understand the truth of Russian life, what it was that linked past and present.

His hope was that Anna Sergeyevna would return from

the hospital and that he could tell her all he had recalled, all he had thought, all he had understood.

And she would share with him the burden, and the clarity, of understanding. This was the consolation for his grief. This was his love.

18

Ivan Grigoryevich often thought about his months in the Lubyanka, and then in the Butyrka.

He had been in the Butyrka three times, but it was the summer of 1937 that he remembered best. At the time he had been in a fog, half unconscious, and it was only now, seventeen years later, that the fog had lifted. Only now could he make out what had happened.

In 1937 the cells had been packed – hundreds of prisoners in a space intended for a few dozen. In the sultry heat of July and August people had been pressed close against one another on the bed boards, dazed and soaked with sweat; it was possible to turn over at night only if they all did it together – at the word of the cell elder, a former commander of a Red Army cavalry division. To get to the *parasha* – the latrine barrel – they had to walk over bodies, and the newcomers to the cell, who slept right next to the *parasha*, were known as 'parachutists'. Sleep – in this cramped and stifling closeness – was more like some kind of swoon, like the delirium of typhus.

The prison walls had seemed to be quivering, like the walls of a boiler almost bursting from some tremendous internal pressure. All night long the Butyrka was humming and throbbing. Outside in the yard cars were delivering new loads of prisoners – all deathly pale as they surveyed this great prison kingdom. And there was the roaring of huge

Black Marias, taking other loads of prisoners away: for further interrogation in the Lubyanka, to be subjected to torture in the Lefortovo,* to the Krasnopresnenskaya transit prison, or to be loaded directly onto a transport for Siberia. If the guards called out to a prisoner, 'With your belongings!', then he knew he was leaving for a camp, and everyone would say their goodbyes to him. The brilliantly lit corridors were full of the shuffling of prisoners' feet and the clanking of the guards' weapons. Prisoners were not allowed to meet. If two escort guards were coming down a corridor towards each other, one would quickly shove his prisoner into one of the cupboard-like boxes that were to be found at regular intervals along the corridor walls. Then he had to wait in the dark until the other prisoner had passed.

The cell windows were covered by thick wooden panels, and light from outside penetrated only through a narrow slit. The prisoners reckoned time not by the sun or the stars but by the prison's internal schedule. The electric lights burned twenty-four hours a day with merciless brightness; it was as if all the terrible, stifling heat came from them, from their white incandescence. Fans hummed night and day, but the torrid air rising off the July asphalt brought no relief. At night the air you breathed seemed like layers of hot felt stuffed inside your lungs and head.

Early in the morning prisoners who had been interrogated during the night were brought back to their cells. Some collapsed in exhaustion on the bed boards; some sobbed and groaned; some sat there motionless, staring in front of them with wide eyes; some rubbed their swollen feet and feverishly recounted what they had been through. Some were so weak that they had to be dragged into the cell by the guards. Others – who had been subjected to continuous interrogation for days on end – were taken on stretchers to the prison hospital. When they were in the investigator's office, prisoners remembered their stifling, stinking cell with fondness, longing to be back among the kind, exhausted faces of their bed board neighbours.

These thousands, these tens of thousands of people – secretaries of district and provincial Party committees; military commissars; heads of political sections; commanding officers of regiments, divisions and entire armies; captains of ships; agronomists; writers; livestock specialists; officials from the Commissariat of Foreign Trade; engineers; ambassadors; Civil War partisans; public prosecutors; chairmen of factory committees; university professors – included representatives of all the social strata suddenly flung up to the surface by the Revolution. As well as Russians there were Belorussians, Ukrainians, Lithuanian and Ukrainian Jews, Armenians, Georgians, slow deliberate Latvians, Poles and people from Central Asia. Whether they had previously been soldiers, workers, peasants, schoolboys, students or artisans, all had taken part in the Revolution and the Civil War. They had smashed the armies of Kornilov and Kaledin, of Kolchak, Denikin, Yudenich and Wrangel, and had poured in their thousands from the most remote towns and villages into the very heart of Russia, into the heart of a country that had become a wasteland. The Revolution abolished all kinds of restrictions – the *numerus clausus*,* property qualifications, various aristocratic privileges, the Pale of Settlement* – and hundreds of thousands of people from all walks of life, from Jewish shtetls and from towns and villages all over Russia took charge of committees, organs and soviets of every kind: of district and provincial Chekas, of RevKoms, UKoms and GubProdKoms, of KomBeds, PolitProsvets and SovNarKhozes.* They began to build a State such as the world had never seen. Cruelty, murders, deprivations of every kind – all this was of no account. It was, after all, being carried out in the name of Russia and of labouring humanity, in the name of the happiness of the working class.

Then came the 1930s. The young men who had taken part in the Civil War were now in their forties, with greying hair. The time of the Revolution, of Committees of the Poor, of the First and Second Congresses of the Comintern was their youth; it was the happiest, most romantic period of their life. They now worked in offices with telephones and secretaries; they had exchanged their military tunics for jackets and ties; they travelled about by car and had consultations with famous doctors; they had learned to appreciate good wines and the joys of holidays in spa towns like Kislovodsk; but, in spite of all this, the days of pointed Budyonny helmets and leather jackets, of millet porridge, of boots full of holes, of the world commune and ideals of unbounded, planetary scope – those days remained the high point of their lives. It was not for the sake of dachas and cars of their own that they had built a new State. This new State had been built for the sake of the Revolution. It was in the name of the Revolution and of a new Russia, free of landowners and capitalists, that sacrifices had been exacted, acts of cruelty committed and blood shed.

The generation of Soviet citizens that disappeared between 1936 and 1939 was not, of course, monolithic.

The first to disappear were the fanatics, the destroyers of the old world, those whose verve and zeal, whose devotion to the Revolution was embodied in the hatred they bore its enemies.

They hated the bourgeoisie, the nobility, the petits bourgeois, the Mensheviks and Socialist Revolutionaries – all of them traitors to the working class. They hated the prosperous peasantry; opportunists of every kind; former tsarist officers being taken on to serve as 'military specialists' in the Red Army; mercenary bourgeois art; venal university lecturers who had sold out to the bourgeoisie; dandies who wore ties; doctors engaged in private practice; women who powdered their noses and strutted about in silk stockings; foppish, reactionary students who only pretended to support the Revolution; priests and rabbis; engineers with cockade caps; poets who, like Fet, wrote decadent little verses about the beauty of nature. They hated Karl Kautsky and Ramsay MacDonald. They did not read Bernstein, but to them he seemed an appalling figure, although his notorious evolutionary-socialist formula, 'The goal is nothing, movement is everything', turned out, in the end, to have encapsulated their fate.

They destroyed the old world and longed for a new world, but they did not build this new world themselves. The hearts of these people – people who made the earth stream with blood, people who hated so many different things and with such passion – were childishly innocent. They were the hearts of fanatics, the hearts – perhaps – of madmen. They hated for the sake of love.

They were the dynamite that the Party used to destroy the old Russia, to make space for the foundation pits of grandiose new constructions, for the granite of a new State.

Soon after these people, the first builders appeared. Their zeal was directed to the creation of a Party and State apparatus, to the construction of plants and factories, to the laying of roads and railways, to the digging of canals, to the mechanisation of Soviet agriculture.

These were the first 'Red merchants', the fathers of Soviet cast iron, of Soviet calico, of Soviet aeroplanes. Not noticing whether it was day or night, heedless of the Siberian cold or the heat of the Kara-Kum Desert, they dug the foundations and raised the walls of new Soviet skyscrapers.

Gvakhariya, Frankfurt, Zavenyagin, Gugel . . .

Among these were some few who died a natural death.

And then there were the Party leaders who built up and governed the various Soviet national republics, territories and provinces: Postyshev, Kirov, Vareikis, Betal Kalmykov, Faizulla Khodzhaev, Mendel Khatayevich, Eikhe . . .

Not one of these died a natural death.

They were vivid, brilliant people: orators; connoisseurs of books, poetry and philosophy; lovers of hunting, feasting and drinking.

Their telephones rang all day and all night; their secretaries worked in three shifts; but unlike the fanatics and dreamers these men knew how to enjoy life. They enjoyed spacious, sun-filled dachas; they enjoyed hunting mountain goats and wild boar; they enjoyed long, merry Sunday dinners; they knew how to appreciate Armenian cognacs and Georgian wines. They no longer wore leather jackets in winter, and the gabardine of their Stalinesque soldiers' tunics was more expensive than woollen cloth from England.

What was remarkable about these men was their energy, their strength of will and their complete inhumanity. All of them – those who loved nature, those who loved poetry and music, those who loved feasting and drinking – were inhuman.

They had no doubt that the new world was being built for the people. It did not trouble them that it was the people themselves – the workers, the peasants, the intelligentsia – who constituted the most insuperable obstacle to the building of this new world.

Sometimes it seemed that the immense energy with which these leaders of the new world were endowed – their iron wills and their capacity for boundless cruelty – was being expended to only one end: to force half-starving people to work with never a day off, beyond their strength, for beggarly pay, while being quartered in primitive barracks and paying every possible kind of tax, levy, loan and assessment on a scale never before seen in history.

But men were building what no man needed. All of these

projects – the White Sea Canal, the Arctic mines, the railways constructed north of the Arctic Circle, the vast factories hidden in the Siberian taiga, the superpowerful hydroelectric power stations deep in the wilderness – were of no use to anyone. It often seemed that these factories, these canals and artificial seas in the desert were of no use even to the Soviet State, let alone to human beings. Sometimes it seemed that the only purpose of these vast constructions was to bind millions of people with the shackles of labour.

Marx, Lenin (his greatest prophet) and Stalin (their great successor and developer of their work) all saw the primacy of economics over politics as the most fundamental truth of their revolutionary doctrine.

And not one of these builders of a new world gave any thought to the fact that by building vast factories that were useless to human beings and often to the State as well, they were overturning Marx's thesis.

The State created by Lenin and consolidated by Stalin was founded not on economics but on politics.

It was politics that determined the content of Stalin's five-year plans. Every one of Stalin's actions – as well as those of his Soviet of People's Commissars, his GosPlan or State Planning Committee, his People's Commissariat of Heavy Industry, his People's Commissariat of Agriculture, his Committee for Grain Procurements, his People's Commissariat for Trade – constituted an absolute triumph of politics over economics.

The builders of the new world did not think – as during the Civil War – that they were accomplishing a world revolution, constructing a universal commune. But they believed that Socialism in One Country,* in a new, young Russia, was at least the dawn of the day of universal socialism.

And then came 1937 – and the prisons were filled with hundreds of thousands of people from the generation of the

Revolution and the Civil War. It was they who had defended the Soviet State – they were both the fathers of this State and its children. And now it was they who were being taken into the prisons they had built for the enemies of the new Russia. They themselves had created the new order and endowed it with terrible power – and now this terrible chastising might, the might of dictatorship, was being unleashed against them. They themselves had forged the sword of the Revolution – and now this sword was falling on their heads. To many of them it seemed as if they had entered a time of chaos and insanity.

Why were they being forced to confess to crimes they had never committed? Why had they been declared enemies of the people? Why were they being cast out from the life they had built, the life they had defended in battle?

It seemed mad to them that they were being equated with those whom they hated and despised, with those they had destroyed as fanatically and mercilessly as if they were rabid dogs.

In the prison cells and camp barracks they found themselves beside Mensheviks whom they had failed to finish off, beside former factory owners and landowners.

Some believed that there had been a *coup d'état*, that their enemies had seized power – and that these enemies, while continuing to make use of Soviet language and Soviet concepts, were now settling accounts with those who had conceived and created the Soviet State.

Sometimes a former district Party committee secretary would end up in the same cell as the district Party committee secretary before him, whom he had himself unmasked as an enemy of the people; and then, a month later, yet another Party committee secretary from the same district would join them on the bed boards. He too, the unmasker of the previous secretary, had now been unmasked. Words and sounds of all

166

kinds were becoming jumbled together: the clatter and clanking of the trains heading north; the barking of guard dogs; the squeaking of boots and ladies' summer shoes on the crunchy taiga snow; the scratching of investigators' pens; spades grating against frozen earth as *zeks* dug graves for other *zeks* who had died from scurvy, from the cold, from heart attacks; people's repentant appeals, at Party meetings, to be treated with clemency; people with white, dead lips, repeating after the investigator the words, 'I confess that, having become a paid agent of foreign intelligence, inspired by a ferocious hatred of everything Soviet, I was preparing to commit acts of terrorism against Soviet statesmen and at the same time supplying secret information . . .'

Only partially muffled by the thick stone of the Lefortovo or the Butyrka, there was a constant crackle of rifle and pistol shots: nine grams of lead in the chest or the back of the head for the thousands, for the tens of thousands of innocents discovered to have committed 'especially vicious acts of espionage or terrorism'.

And those builders of the new world who were still free kept on trying to divine: 'Will they, won't they?' Everyone was waiting for a knock on the door in the night, the whisper of car tyres outside the building, and then a sudden silence.

And so, in chaos and absurdity, in the madness of false accusations, the generation of the Civil War disappeared. New days began, and new actors appeared on the stage . . .

19

Mekler, Lev Naumovich . . . He had used to wear size 45 shoes and a size 58 suit from the Moscow Tailoring Combine.* And now he had been sentenced under Article 58: betrayal of the motherland, terrorism, sabotage, never mind a few other things.

He had not been shot, probably because he was one of the first to be arrested. At that time death sentences had not been handed out so liberally.

Stumbling, squinting short-sightedly and distractedly, he had gone through all the circles of the prison and camp hell. He had not perished because an inner fire – the faith that had consumed him since adolescence – had protected him from scurvy and from malnutrition, from bitter winds and from nights when the temperature fell to forty degrees below zero. Nor had he died of dysentery; nor had he perished when a barge packed with prisoners sank in the Yenisey.

He had not had his throat cut by the common criminals. He had not been tortured to death in a punishment cell or beaten to death during interrogation. He had not been shot during a mass purge, at a time when every tenth prisoner was being shot.

Where had this powerful flame of fanaticism come from? How had it appeared in this son of a sad, sly shopkeeper from the shtetl of Fastov? How had it sprung up in a young man who had studied in a commercial school and who had been brought up on the 'Golden Library' and on the adventure stories of Louis Boussenard?* What had instilled him with this hatred of capitalism? Neither he nor his father, after all, had spent years down mines or in factories filled with smoke and dust.

Who or what had given him the soul of a fighter? The example of Zhelyabov and Kalyaev? The wisdom of *The Communist Manifesto*? The sufferings of the poor next door?

Or had these coals been smouldering deep in the millennial abyss of heredity, ready to burst into flame in the struggle against Caesar's soldiers or against the Spanish Inquisition, in the hunger and intellectual frenzy of Talmud Torah schools,* in a shtetl's attempt to defend itself during a pogrom?

Maybe it was indeed these thousands of years of humiliation, the anguish of exile in Babylon, the humiliations of the shtetl, the poverty of the Pale of Settlement, that had engendered the frenzy for justice which had forged the soul of the Bolshevik Lev Mekler?

His inability to adapt to everyday life evoked both mockery and admiration. To some there had seemed something saintly about this Komsomol leader in torn sandals, in a calico shirt with an open collar, with nothing on his head but his curly hair – and he had seemed no less saintly as a regimental commissar wearing a torn leather jacket and a peaked Budyonny helmet with a red star that had faded as if from loss of blood. And he had been no less unshaven and ragged when, as Commissar of Justice for the entire Ukraine, he had got out of his car in a tattered raincoat with missing buttons and walked, in winter, to his office.

He had seemed helpless, as if not of this world, but there were some who remembered how reverently they had listened to him during stormy meetings at the front, how they had then followed him through the fire of Wrangel's machine guns.

He was a preacher, an apostle, a soldier of the world socialist revolution. For the sake of the Revolution he was ready, without a second thought, to give up everything – his life, the love of a woman, all those nearest and dearest to him. The only thing it was impossible for him to give up was happiness – since nothing could have brought him more happiness than to go to the stake for the Revolution, to sacrifice for her everything on earth that a human being holds dear.

The future world order seemed to him infinitely splendid, and for its sake Mekler was ready to employ the most pitiless violence.

He was, essentially, a kind-hearted man. If a mosquito was sucking his blood, rather than crushing it with a slap of the hand, he would send it on its way with a delicate flick of his fingers. If he caught a bedbug at the scene of the crime, he would wrap it in a piece of paper and carry it outside.

What distinguished his service to the Revolution and to the good of humanity was his lack of pity for suffering and his readiness to shed blood.

In his revolutionary purity he imprisoned his father and testified against him before the Cheka. And when his sister begged him to defend her husband, who had been arrested as a saboteur, he turned his back on her cruelly and sullenly.

In his meekness he was pitiless towards those who held the wrong views. To him the Revolution seemed helpless and childishly trustful – surrounded as she was by treachery, the cruelty of the wicked and villainous, the filth of those who wished to corrupt her.

And so he was pitiless towards the enemies of the Revolution.

On his revolutionary conscience was only one stain. Without telling the Party, he had given help to his old mother, the widow of a man who had been shot by the organs of justice. And, after her death, he had paid for her to be given a religious funeral; that had been her last, pathetic wish.

His vocabulary, his way of thinking, his actions all sprang from one and the same source: the books written in the name of the Revolution, the justice and morality of the Revolution, the poetry of the Revolution and the strategy of the Revolution – her marching soldiers, her visions, her songs.

It was through the eyes of the Revolution that he looked at the stars in the sky and at birch leaves in April; it was from her most sweet cup that he drank the charm, the potion of first love; it was in the light of her wisdom that he understood the battle in ancient Rome between patricians and slaves, the struggle between landowners and serfs, the class warfare between factory owners and the proletariat. The Revolution was his mother, his tender beloved, his sun, his destiny.

And now the Revolution had put him in a cell in the Lubyanka and knocked out eight of his teeth. Swearing obscenely and calling him a mangy Yid, stamping on him with officer's boots, she had demanded that he, her son, her beloved apostle, should confess himself to be her secret and mortal enemy, her would-be poisoner.

He did not, of course, renounce the Revolution. During conveyor-belt interrogations lasting a hundred hours his faith did not waver for even a moment; his faith did not waver when he lay on the floor and saw the polished toe of a box-calf boot beside his blood-filled mouth. The Revolution was coarse, obtuse and cruel as she interrogated him under torture; she was enraged by the loyalty, by the meek patience of the Old Bolshevik Lev Mekler.

Her rage was the rage of a man trying to drive away a dog, a dog that belongs to him, a mongrel dog that won't stop following at his heels. First he quickens his steps; then he shouts at the dog and stamps his feet; then he shakes his fist at the dog and throws stones at it. The dog runs away, but when, a hundred yards further on, the man looks round, he sees the now crippled dog hurriedly limping after him – as determinedly faithful as ever.

And what the man finds most abhorrent of all is the look in those doggy eyes – so meek, so sad and loving, so fanatical in their devotion.

The dog's love enrages its master. The dog sees this rage and cannot understand it. The dog cannot understand that, while committing an unprecedented injustice, the master wants, at least a little, to appease his conscience. The dog's meekness and devotion have been driving him insane. He hates the dog for this love more than he ever hated the wolves against which the dog once defended the house where he had lived as a young man. Through his coarse brutality, he is hoping to put an end to this love.

Shocked by this sudden, inexplicable cruelty, the dog keeps on following the master.

Why? Why?

And the dog cannot understand that there is nothing absurd or senseless about this sudden hatred; the dog cannot understand that everything is real and rational.*

This hatred is normal and predictable; it is an expression of a clear, mathematical logic. To the dog, however, it seems like a spell of madness. It all seems wild and senseless, and the dog even feels anxious on the master's behalf. The dog wants to rescue the master from his blindness – for the master's sake, not for its own. And the dog loves the master and therefore cannot leave him.

And the master understands now that the dog is not going to leave him. The master knows now that the only thing he can do is to strangle the dog or shoot it.

And in order that this execution – this execution of a dog

that adores and idolises him – should not weigh on his conscience or evoke the disapproval of his neighbours, the master decides that this dog must be turned into an enemy, into an artificial enemy. Let the dog confess, before dying, that it wished to tear its master to pieces.

It is easier to kill an enemy than to kill a friend.

In that first house, after all – in the house he built in his youth in the midst of gloomy and deserted ruins, in the house where he once prayed with a pure heart – the dog was his friend and guard, his inseparable companion.

So let the dog confess that it was in cahoots with the wolves.

And in its death agony, as it is being choked with a rope, the dog looks at its master with meek love, with a faith equal to that which led the first Christian martyrs to their deaths.

And the dog never understood one very simple thing: its master had left that house of prayer and youthful intoxication and moved into a building of granite and glass, and his village mongrel had begun to seem an absurdity, a burden. More than a burden – a danger. Which is why he killed it.

20

The years passed, the dust and the fog cleared, and it became possible to make out what had happened. What had once looked like chaos or insanity, like self-destruction, like a chain of absurd coincidences, what had once driven people out of their minds because it seemed so mysteriously and tragically senseless – all this gradually became recognisable as the clear, distinct attributes of a new life, of a new reality.

The fate of the generation of the Revolution now ceased to appear mystical and extraordinary and began to seem entirely logical. And Ivan Grigoryevich felt able, at last, to understand his country's new fate – the fate built on the bones of that generation.

The Bolshevik generation had been forged in the days of the Revolution, in the days when the ideal of a world commune held sway, when people took part in inspired, hungry, voluntary working Saturdays.* That generation took on its shoulders the legacy of the World War and the Civil War – chaos, famine, typhus, anarchy, crime and banditry. Through Lenin's lips it proclaimed that there was a Party which could set Russia on a new path.* Without hesitation, it accepted the inheritance of hundreds of years of Russian despotism, during which dozens of generations had come and gone knowing no rights except that of a master to do as he pleased with his serfs.

Under Lenin's leadership the Bolshevik generation dissolved

the Constituent Assembly and destroyed the democratic revolutionary parties that had struggled against Russian absolutism.

The Bolshevik generation did not – in the context of bourgeois Russia – believe in the value of individual freedom; it did not believe in the value of freedom of speech or of freedom of the press.

Like Lenin, it saw as irrelevant nonsense the freedoms of which the intelligentsia and many revolutionary workers had long dreamed.

The young State destroyed the democratic parties, clearing the way for Soviet construction. By the end of the 1920s, these parties had been liquidated. Men who had been imprisoned under the Tsar were either back in prison or carrying out forced labour.

The year 1930 saw the total collectivisation of agriculture – an axe raised over the Russian village.

Not long after this the axe was raised yet again. This time, however, it fell on the generation of the Civil War. A few of this generation survived, but its soul, its faith in a world commune, its romantic and revolutionary strength disappeared with those who were destroyed in 1937. Those who were left, those who went on living and working, managed to adapt to the new time and its new people.

The new people did not believe in the Revolution. They were the children not of the Revolution, but of the new State that the Revolution had created.

The new State had no need of holy apostles, of frenzied, possessed builders, of faithful disciples. The new State no longer even needed servants; it needed employees. And the State's only misgiving with regard to these employees was that they did, on occasion, turn out to be very petty-minded indeed – and thieving rascals into the bargain.

Terror and dictatorship swallowed up their creators.

The State, previously seen as a means, had now proved to be an end in itself. The creators of this State had seen it as a means of realising their ideals. It turned out, however, that their dreams and ideals had been a means employed by a great and terrible State. The State was no longer a servant but a grim autocrat. It was not the people who needed the Red Terror of 1919. It was not the people who did away with freedom of speech and freedom of the press. It was not the people who needed the death of millions of peasants – most of the people, after all, *were* peasants. It was not the people who chose, in 1937, to fill the prisons and camps. It was not the people who needed the murderous deportations, the resettlement in Siberia and Central Asia, of the Crimean Tatars, Kalmyks, Balkars, Chechens and Volga Germans, of Russified Bulgarians and Greeks. Nor was it the people who destroyed the workers' right to strike or the peasants' right to sow what they chose. It was not the people who added huge taxes to the price of consumer goods.

The State became the master. The national element left the realm of form and entered the realm of content; it became what was most central and most essential, turning the socialist element into a mere wrapping, a verbal husk, an empty shell.

Thus, with tragic clarity, was made manifest a sacred law of life: human freedom stands above everything. There is no end in the world for the sake of which it is permissible to sacrifice human freedom.

21

It was strange. When Ivan Grigoryevich remembered the year 1937, and the women who had been sentenced to hard labour because of their husbands; when he recalled Anna Sergeyevna's account of total collectivisation and the famine in the Ukrainian countryside; when he thought about the laws according to which workers were sent to prison for getting to work twenty minutes late and peasants were sentenced to eight years in the camps for hiding a few grains of wheat; when Ivan Grigoryevich contemplated these things, it was not a man with a moustache, not a man wearing a military tunic and boots, whom he saw in his mind's eye. No, it was not Stalin he saw in his mind's eye but Lenin.

It was as if Lenin's life had not come to an end on 21 January 1924.

Now and again Ivan Grigoryevich wrote down his thoughts about Lenin and Stalin in a school exercise book left behind by Alyosha.

All the victories of the Party and the State were associated with the name of Lenin. But Lenin also seemed responsible for all the terrible acts of cruelty carried out in the country.

The tragedies of the countryside, the year 1937, the new bureaucracy, the new bourgeoisie, forced labour – all of these found their justification in Lenin's revolutionary passion, in Lenin's speeches, articles and appeals.

And little by little, over the years, Lenin's features changed. The image of the young student called Volodya Ulyanov, of the young Marxist who went by the name of Tulin, of the Siberian exile, of the revolutionary émigré, of the political writer and thinker called Vladimir Ilyich Lenin; the image of the man who had proclaimed the era of the world socialist revolution; the image of the creator of a revolutionary dictatorship in Russia, the man who had liquidated every revolutionary party in Russia except the one that seemed to him the most revolutionary of all; the image of the man who had dissolved the Constituent Assembly, which represented every class and party of post-revolutionary Russia, and who had created soviets on which only revolutionary workers and peasants were to be represented – this image changed. Features familiar from portraits changed; the image of the first Soviet head of state changed.

Lenin's work continued – and as it acquired new features, so the image of the dead Lenin acquired new features.

Lenin was an intellectual. His family belonged to the working intelligentsia. His brothers and sisters belonged to the revolutionary movement. His elder brother, Aleksandr, became a hero and holy martyr of the Revolution.

Memoirists all recall that, even as the leader of the Revolution, as the creator of the Party, as the head of the Soviet government, he remained modest and simple. He did not smoke or drink and, in all probability, he never in his life cursed and swore at someone in truly foul language. There was a student purity about his idea of leisure: music, the theatre, books, walks. He always dressed democratically, almost as if he were poor.

The little Volodya so loved by his mother and sisters, the young man who listened to the 'Appassionata'* and read and reread *War and Peace*, the young man who wore a crumpled tie and an old jacket and always sat in the gallery when he went to the theatre – can this really have been the founder of a State that chose to adorn the chests of Yagoda, Yezhov, Beria, Merkulov and Abakumov with its highest honour, with his very own Order of Lenin?

On the anniversary of Lenin's death the Order of Lenin was awarded to Lidia Timashuk. Was this an indication that Lenin's cause had dried and withered – or that it was truly triumphing?

Five-Year Plans passed. Decades passed. Events of incandescent immediacy cooled and hardened. Encased by the cement of time, they turned into great slabs – into the history of the Soviet State.

> No artist has painted
> A true portrait of Lenin.
> Ages to come will complete
> Lenin's unfinished portrait.*

Did Poletaev understand the tragic implication of his lines about Lenin? The character traits emphasised by the authors of memoirs and biographies, character traits which once seemed crucial and which charmed millions of minds and hearts – these traits proved in the end to be entirely incidental to the course of history. The history of the Russian State did not choose these human and humane sides of Lenin's character but cast them aside as unwanted rubbish. The history of the State did not need the Lenin who admired *War and Peace* and who listened to the 'Appassionata' with his face buried in his hands. It did not need Lenin's modest and democratic tastes; it did not need his warmth and attentiveness towards drivers and secretaries; nor did it need his conversations with peasant children, his kindness towards domestic animals or the deep pain he felt when Julius Martov ceased to be his friend and became his enemy.

But everything about Lenin that had been seen as temporary and accidental, everything that had been put down to the particular circumstances of the revolutionary underground and the desperate struggles of the first Soviet years – all this turned out to be of lasting, defining importance.

The authors of memoirs say nothing about the aspect of Lenin's character that led him to order a search of Georgy Plekhanov's apartment as he lay dying, but it is this aspect of Lenin's character – the aspect that determined his total intolerance of political democracy – which proved dominant.

A man who has gone up in the world, a merchant or factory owner from a peasant family who now lives in a mansion of his own and travels on his private yacht – such a man may still display peasant traits; he may still love kvass, pickled-cabbage soup and crude, vivid popular expressions. A field marshal in gold braid may still like to roll his own cigarettes from *makhorka*; he may still enjoy the ribald humour of soldiers.

But do these traits, do these tastes and fond memories matter to the millions whose fates are determined by the factories owned by the ex-peasant, by the movements of share prices or armies?

It is not through love of pickled-cabbage soup and *makhorka* that an industrialist acquires wealth or a general wins glory.

The author of one memoir about Lenin* describes going for a Sunday walk with him in the Swiss mountains. Out of breath after a steep climb, they reached a summit and sat down on a rock. The young woman thought that Vladimir Ilyich's intent gaze was taking in every smallest detail of the beautiful Alpine landscape. She felt moved and excited, thinking of the poetry that was flooding his soul. All of a sudden he sighed and said, 'These Mensheviks – they're really fouling things up for us!'

This charming little story tells us a lot about Lenin. On one side of the scales – the whole of creation. On the other side of the scales – the Party.

October selected those of Vladimir Ilyich's traits that it needed. It cast away those that it did not need.

Throughout its entire history the Russian revolutionary movement included within it the most contradictory qualities. The genuine love for the people to be found in many Russian revolutionaries – men whose meekness and readiness to endure suffering has been seen before only in the early Christians – coexisted with a fierce contempt towards human suffering, an extreme veneration of abstract principles and an implacable determination to destroy not only one's enemies but also one's comrades-in-arms, should their interpretation of these principles differ however minutely from one's own. This sectarian single-mindedness, this readiness to suppress today's living freedom for the sake of a hypothetical future freedom, to transgress ordinary, everyday morality in the name of the future – all of this can be found in Pestel, in Bakunin and Nechaev, and in some of what was said and done by members of the People's Will.

No, it was not only love, not only compassion that led such people along the path of revolution. To find what engendered these people, one needs to look far back into the thousand-year depths of Russian history.

Similar figures existed in previous centuries, but it was the twentieth century that brought them out from the wings and placed them centre stage.

This kind of person is like a surgeon in a hospital ward. His interest in the patients and their families, his jokes, the arguments he takes part in, his struggles on behalf of homeless children and his concern for workers who have reached the age of retirement – all this is unimportant, trifling, a mere husk. His soul lies in his surgeon's knife.

What is most important about this man is his fanatical faith in the omnipotence of the surgeon's knife. It is the surgeon's knife that is the twentieth century's true theoretician, its greatest philosophical leader.

During the fifty-four years of his life Lenin did more than listen to the 'Appassionata', reread *War and Peace*, have heart-to-heart talks with peasant delegates, admire the Russian landscape and worry about whether his secretary had a proper winter coat. This goes without saying; it should be no surprise that Lenin possessed a real face, not only an image.

And one can imagine Lenin giving expression to any number of different character traits and peculiarities in his daily life – in that daily life that we all inevitably lead, whether we are dentists, leaders of nations, or cutters in a ladies' clothing workshop.

These traits can manifest themselves at any moment of night or day, as a man washes his face in the morning, as he eats his porridge, as he looks out through the window at a pretty woman whose skirt has been caught by the wind, as he uses a match to pick his teeth, as he feels jealous about his wife or tries to make her feel jealous about him, as he looks at his bare legs in the bathhouse and scratches his armpits, as he reads scraps of newspaper in the toilet, trying to piece a torn page together, as he farts and at once tries to mask the sound by coughing or humming.

Such moments occur in the lives of both the great and the small, and they can, of course, be found in Lenin's life.

Maybe Lenin developed a paunch because he ate too much macaroni and butter, preferring it to vegetables.

Maybe he and his wife had arguments, unknown to the world, about how often he washed his feet or brushed his teeth, or about his reluctance to change a worn shirt with a dirty collar.

And it may indeed be possible to break through the fortifications surrounding a supposedly human but in reality unreal and exalted image of the leader. It may be possible, by making quick, sudden dashes – or by creeping silently along on your stomach – to reach a true, authentic Lenin that no memoirist has described.

But what would we gain from knowing the hidden truth of Lenin's behaviour in bathroom, bedroom or dining room? Would this help us towards a deeper understanding of Lenin the leader of the new Russia, the founder of a new world order? Would we be able to find any real correlation between Lenin as a human being and the nature of the State he founded? In order to establish such a correlation, we would have to assume that Lenin behaved in the same way as a political leader as he did in his everyday life. This assumption, however, would be arbitrary and mistaken; such correlations, after all, are as likely to be inverse as to be direct – people behave differently in different spheres of their life.

In his personal relationships – when he gave someone help, when he stayed the night with friends or went out for a walk with them – Lenin was always polite, sensitive and kind. Yet Lenin was always rude, harsh and implacable towards his political opponents. He never admitted the least possibility that they might be even partially right, that he might be even partially wrong.

'Venal . . . lackey . . . groveller . . . hireling . . . agent . . . a Judas bought for thirty pieces of silver . . .' – these were the words Lenin used of his opponents.

It was never Lenin's aim, in a dispute, to win his opponent over to his own views. He did not even truly address his opponent; the people for whom his words were intended were the witnesses to the dispute. Lenin's aim was always to ridicule his opponent, to compromise him in the eyes of witnesses. These witnesses might be a few close friends; they might be an audience of a thousand conference delegates; or they might be the million readers of a newspaper article.

Lenin's concern in an argument was not with truth but with victory. He needed, at all costs, to be victorious – and to this end he was happy to employ any rhetorical means. He was equally ready to trip his opponent from behind, to give him a metaphorical slap in the face or to daze him with a metaphorical blow on the head.

It is clear that Lenin's behaviour in his private, everyday life had no connection with how he behaved as the leader of a new world order.

And when the dispute moved from the pages of newspapers and magazines to the streets, when it moved to military battlefields or to fields of rye – then too there was nothing that Lenin shrank from, no tactics too vicious for him to employ.

Lenin's intolerance, his unshakeable drive to achieve his purpose, his contempt for freedom, his brutality towards those who did not share his views, his unwavering readiness to wipe off the face of the earth not only fortresses but also whole districts, regions and provinces that challenged his view of the truth – all this was a part of Lenin long before October. All this was deep-rooted; all these aspects of Lenin's character and behaviour were present in the young Volodya Ulyanov.

All his abilities, all his will and passion were directed towards one end: the seizure of power.

To this end he sacrificed everything. In order to seize power he sacrificed what was most holy in Russia: her freedom. This freedom was childishly helpless; it was inexperienced and naive. How could this eight-month-old baby, born in a land with a heritage of a thousand years of slavery – how could this infant freedom have been anything but naive?

The cultured, intellectual side of Lenin – which had once seemed what was deepest and truest about him – always receded into the background as soon as the going got difficult. Lenin's true character then manifested itself in his iron will – in his frenzied, unyielding strength of will.

What led Lenin along the path of revolution? Love for human beings? A wish to put an end to the misery of the peasantry, to the workers' poverty and lack of rights? A faith in the truth of Marxism, in the rectitude of his own Party?

For Lenin, the Russian Revolution had nothing to do with Russian freedom. But the power to which he so passionately aspired was not something he needed personally.

And here we come to something unique about Lenin: the simplicity of his character engendered a certain complexity.

In order to crave power so fiercely, one must be endowed with enormous political ambition. This love of power is something crude and simple. But this driven figure, capable of anything in his pursuit of power, was modest in his private life and it was not to gratify himself that he sought power. Here, Lenin's simplicity ends and his complexity begins.

If we try to imagine a private Lenin who is an exact equivalent of the political Lenin, we will be confronted with a ranting dogmatist – someone harsh and primitive, high-handed, domineering, pitiless, insanely ambitious.

It is frightening even to think of Lenin behaving in this way in his everyday life – towards his friends and family, towards someone he shared an apartment with.

But that is not how it was. The private man turned out to be the inverse of the man on the world stage. Plus and minus, minus and plus.

And the overall picture turns out to be very different; it turns out to be complicated, in some ways tragic.

Insane political ambition alongside an old jacket, a glass of weak tea, a student garret.

The ability to trample one's opponent into the mud without a second thought, to deafen and stun him during an argument, combined with a sweet smile, with a shy sensitivity.

Implacable cruelty, a contempt for freedom – the holy of holies of the Russian Revolution – along with a pure, youthful delight in fine music or a good book.

Lenin . . . First there is the deified image. Then there is the image created by his enemies – a uniform image, an image that has him behaving as harshly and cruelly in his everyday life as in his role as leader of the new world order. Finally, there is a third image – an image that seems to me to be closer to reality but which is not easy to comprehend.

22

In order to understand Lenin, we have to do more than examine his qualities as a politician or the qualities he showed in everyday life. We have to correlate Lenin's character first with the supposed national character of the Russian people and then with the overall thrust of Russian history.

In his asceticism and natural modesty, Lenin had an affinity with Russian pilgrims. In his faith and directness, he answered to the folk ideal of a religious teacher. In his attachment to Russian nature, to its forests and meadows, he was akin to the Russian peasantry. His receptivity to Hegel and Marx and Western thought as a whole, his ability to absorb and give expression to the spirit of the West, was the manifestation of a peculiarly Russian trait first pointed out by Chaadaev. It is the same universal sympathy, the same astonishing ability to enter deep into the spirit of another nation, that Dostoevsky famously saw in Pushkin. This receptivity makes Lenin akin both to Pushkin and to Peter the Great.

Lenin's fanatical, possessed quality is similar to the religious faith, the religious frenzy of Avvakum. And Avvakum is an entirely native-born, Russian phenomenon.

In the nineteenth century Russian thinkers looked to the Russian national character, the Russian soul and Russian religious nature for an explanation of Russia's historical path.

Chaadaev, one of the most intelligent figures of that

century, emphasised the ascetic and sacrificial quality of Russian Christianity, its undiluted Byzantine purity.

Dostoevsky saw universality, an aspiration towards the universally human, as the true foundation of the Russian soul.

Twentieth-century Russia loves to repeat the predictions made about it by earlier Russian thinkers and prophets: Gogol, Chaadaev, Belinsky, Dostoevsky.

But who would not like to repeat such things about himself?

The nineteenth-century prophets predicted that Russia would, in the future, lead the spiritual evolution not only of Europe but also of the entire world.

These foretellers were speaking not of Russian military glory but of the glory of the Russian heart, of Russian faith, of the example that Russia would set.

Gogol's flying troika . . . Dostoevsky's 'It is for the Russian soul, all-human and all-unifying, to accommodate within itself, in brotherly love, all our brothers, and, in the end, perhaps, to speak the final word of the great general harmony, of the final brotherly concord of all tribes according to the law of the Gospel of Christ . . .'* Chaadaev's 'Then we will naturally take our place as one of the nations chosen to influence humanity not only in the capacity of a battering ram but also through the force of ideas . . .' Gogol's 'Russia, are you not also like the bold troika which no one can overtake? The road is a cloud of smoke under your wheels, the bridges thunder . . .'*

And then, in the same letter, Chaadaev brilliantly put his finger on a striking feature of Russian history: 'the enormous fact of the gradual enslavement of our peasantry, which can only be seen as the strictly logical consequence of our entire history'.*

The implacable suppression of the individual personality

– its total, servile, subjection to the sovereign and the State – has been a constant feature of Russian history. This too was recognised by the Russian prophets.

But along with the suppression of the individual by prince, landowner, sovereign and State, the Russian prophets sensed a purity, profundity and clarity unknown to the Western world. They saw a Christlike power – the power of the Russian soul – and they prophesied a great and brilliant future for this soul. These prophets all agreed that the Christian ideal had been embodied in the Russian soul in an ascetic, Byzantine, anti-Western manner – in a way quite independent of the State – and that the forces inherent in the Russian soul would manifest themselves as a powerful influence on the peoples of Europe. They believed that these forces would purify and transform the life of the Western world, enlightening it in the spirit of brotherhood, and that the Western world would joyfully and trustingly follow this Russian man who was so universal in his humanity. These prophecies of Russia's most powerful minds and hearts had one fatal flaw in common. They all saw the power of the Russian soul and its significance for the world, but they all failed to see that this soul had been a slave for a thousand years, that its peculiarities had been engendered by the absence of freedom. However all-powerful you are, what can you give to the world if you have been a slave for a thousand years?

The nineteenth century, however, seemed at last to have brought closer the time foretold by the Russian prophets, the time when Russia, always so receptive to other teachings and other examples, always so greedy to absorb other spiritual influences, was herself preparing to act on the world.

For a hundred years Russia had been drinking in a borrowed idea of freedom. For a hundred years – through the lips of Pestel, Ryleyev, Herzen, Chernyshevsky, Lavrov, Bakunin; through the lips of her writers; through the lips of such martyrs as Zhelyabov, Sofya Perovskaya, Timofey Mikhailov and Kibalchich; through the lips of Plekhanov, Kropotkin and Mikhailovsky; through the lips of Sazonov and Kalyaev; through the lips of Lenin, Martov and Chernov; through the lips of her classless intelligentsia; through the lips of her students and progressive workers – for a hundred years Russia had been imbibing the work of the thinkers and philosophers of Western freedom. This thinking was brought to Russia by books, by university faculties, by young men who had studied in Paris and Heidelberg. It was brought to Russia by the boots of Napoleon's soldiers. It was brought to Russia by engineers and enlightened merchants. It was brought in by impoverished Westerners who came to Russia to work and whose sense of their own innate human dignity evoked the envious astonishment of Russian princes.

And so, fertilised by the ideas of freedom and of the dignity of man, the Russian Revolution ran its course.

And what did the Russian soul do with these Western ideas? How did she transform them within herself? Into what kind of crystal did she make them precipitate? What kind of shoot would she cause to spring from the subconscious of history?

'Russia, where are you hurtling to? . . . There is no answer.'

Dozens, perhaps hundreds, of revolutionary teachings and creeds, leaders and parties, programmes and prophecies came as suitors to the young Russia who had cast off the chains of tsarism. As they paraded before her, the captains of Russian progress gazed longingly, passionately and pleadingly into her face.

And then there they stood in a great circle – moderates, fanatics, labourists, populists, friends of the workers, advocates of the peasantry, liberal factory owners, light-seeking men of the Church, crazy anarchists.

Invisible threads – ties that even they themselves were

often unable to sense – bound these men to the ideals of Western parliaments and constitutional monarchies, to the ideals of erudite cardinals and bishops, to the ideals of factory owners and educated landowners, to the ideals of preachers, university professors and trade union leaders.

The slave girl's gaze, the great slave girl's searching, doubting, evaluating gaze came to rest on Lenin. It was him she chose.

As in an old fairy tale, he guessed her hidden thought. He interpreted her perplexing dream, her innermost secret.

But was it really like that?

He became her chosen one not only because she chose him but also because he chose her.

She followed him because he promised her mountains of gold and rivers flowing with wine. Willingly at first, trustfully, she followed him along a merry, intoxicating path lit by the burning estates of landowners. Then she began to stumble, to look back, ever more terrified of the path now stretching before her – but the grip of the iron hand that led her was growing tighter and tighter.

And he, imbued with apostolic faith, walked on, leading Russia behind him, failing to realise that he had succumbed to a strange delusion. In Russia's obedient walk, in her renewed, post-revolutionary submissiveness, in her maddening pliancy, everything that he had brought her from the revolutionary, freedom-loving West was being transformed. Everything he had brought to Russia was drowning and perishing.

He thought that his unshakeable, dictatorial power guaranteed that the ideal he believed in, the gift he had brought to his country, would be preserved in all its purity.

He rejoiced in this power. He identified it with the justice of his faith – and then, for one terrible moment, he realised that his unyielding strength as the leader of a country so gentle, a country so submissive and easily influenced, was really a supreme form of impotence.

And the tighter his grip, the sterner his stride, the more obedient Russia became to his educated and revolutionary violence – the less power Lenin possessed to struggle against the truly satanic force of Russia's serf past.

Like some thousand-year-old alcoholic solution, the principle of slavery in the Russian soul had only grown stronger. Like aqua regia, smoking from its own strength, it dissolved the metal and salt of human dignity, entirely changing the inner life of Russian man.

Throughout nine hundred years Russia's vast spaces – which appeared, on a superficial view, to have engendered a sweeping breadth of soul, a sense of daring and freedom – were no more than a mute alembic for slavery.

Throughout nine hundred years Russia appeared to be moving away from remote forest settlements, from smoke-filled huts without chimneys, from the distant hermitages of breakaway sects, from log palaces. Throughout nine hundred years Russia's future seemed to be embodied in the factories of the Urals, of the coal of the Donbass, of the Hermitage Museum and the stone palaces of Petersburg; it seemed to be embodied in powerful artillery, in the metal smiths and lathe operators of Tula, in frigates and steam hammers.

Everything seemed entirely clear; to a superficial observer, there could be no doubt that Russia was moving towards the West and growing in enlightenment.

But the more the surface of Russian life came to resemble the surface of Western life, the more evocative of Western life grew the roar of Russia's factories, the rattle of her carriages, the clickety-clack of her train wheels, the flapping sails of her ships and the crystal gleam of her palace windows – the deeper became the hidden abyss that separated the inner-most essence of Russian life from that of Western life.

The evolution of the West was fertilised by the growth of freedom; Russia's evolution was fertilised by the growth of slavery. This is the abyss that divides Russia and the West.

The history of humanity is the history of human freedom. The growth of human potential is expressed, above all, in the growth of freedom. Freedom is not, as Engels claimed, 'the recognition of necessity'. Freedom is the direct opposite of necessity; freedom is necessity overcome. Progress, in essence, is the progress of human freedom. What is life itself, if not freedom? The evolution of life is the evolution of freedom.

Russia has always evolved in a peculiar way; what has evolved has been the degree of non-freedom. Year by year serfdom grew harsher and the peasants' right to their land more tenuous. Meanwhile, Russian science, technology and learning continued to advance, merging with the growth of slavery.

The birth of Russian statehood was marked by the final enslavement of the peasantry; in 1497, 'Autumn Yury's Day', 26 November, the peasant's last day of freedom, was abolished. No longer could a peasant choose to move from one landlord to another.*

After this, the number of free 'wanderers' kept dwindling; the number of serfs continued to grow; and Russia began to make herself felt as a part of Europe. After being tied to the land, the peasant was then tied first to the owner of the land and then to the officials representing the State and the army. The landowner, meanwhile, was granted first the right to pass judgement on his serfs and then the right to subject them to 'the Moscow torture' (as it was christened four centuries ago); this meant tying a man's hands behind his back, lifting him off the ground by his wrists and beating him with a knout. And Russian metallurgy continued to progress; grain warehouses grew larger; the State and its army grew stronger; the world saw the dawn of Russian military glory; and literacy increased.

The remarkable work of Peter the Great, who laid the foundations of Russian scientific and industrial progress, involved an equally remarkable progress in the severity of serfdom. The serfs who worked the land were reduced still further in status – until they enjoyed no more rights than a landlord's household serfs; the few remaining 'wanderers' were enserfed. Peter also enserfed the peasant farmers of the far north and of the southern and eastern frontiers. There was a similar increase in the burdens placed on the peasants owned by the State; this too was in the interests of Petrine enlightenment and progress. Peter believed that he was bringing Russia closer to the West – and that was indeed the case. But the abyss between freedom and non-freedom continued to grow.

Then came the dazzling age of Catherine the Great, the age of a wonderful flowering of Russian arts and Russian enlightenment – and the age when serfdom reached its highest expression.

And so, Russian progress and Russian slavery were shackled together by a thousand-year-long chain. Every move forward towards the light only deepened the black pit of serfdom.

The nineteenth century, however, was a very special century for Russia.

This century shook the fundamental principle of Russian life: the link between progress and serfdom.

Russian revolutionary thinkers failed to appreciate the importance of the emancipation of the serfs in 1861. The emancipation of the serfs – as we can see from the history of the following century – was more truly revolutionary than the October Revolution. The emancipation of the serfs shook Russia's thousand-year-old foundation, a foundation left entirely intact by both Peter the Great and Lenin: the dependence of the country's evolution on the growth of slavery.

After the emancipation of the serfs, the revolutionary leaders, the students and the intelligentsia fought violently, passionately and with self-abnegation for a human dignity that Russia had never known, for progress without slavery. This new principle was entirely alien to Russian tradition, and no one knew what would become of Russia if she were to renounce the thousand-year link between her evolution and slavery. No one knew what would become of the Russian character.

In February 1917, the path of freedom lay open for Russia. Russia chose Lenin.

The destruction of Russian life carried out by Lenin was on a vast scale. Lenin destroyed the way of life of the landowners. Lenin destroyed factory owners and merchants.

Nevertheless, Lenin was fated by history. However bizarre this may sound, he was fated by Russian history to preserve Russia's old curse: this link between progress and non-freedom.

The only true revolutionaries are those who seek to destroy the very foundation of the old Russia: her slave soul.

And so it was that Lenin's obsession with revolution, his fanatical faith in the truth of Marxism and absolute intolerance of any dissent, all led him to advance hugely the development of the Russia he hated with all his fanatical soul.

It is, indeed, tragic that a man who so sincerely loved Tolstoy and Beethoven should have helped to bring about a new enslavement of the peasants and workers, that he should have played a central role in reducing to the status of lackeys – State lackeys – such outstanding figures of Russian culture as the writer Aleksey Tolstoy, the physical chemist Nikolay Semyonov, and the composer Dmitry Shostakovich.

The debate initiated by the supporters of Russian freedom was finally concluded. Once again, Russian slavery proved invincible.

Lenin's victory became his defeat.

But Lenin's tragedy was not only a Russian tragedy. It became a tragedy for the whole world.

Did Lenin ever imagine the true consequences of his revolution? Did he ever imagine that it would not simply be a matter of Russia now leading the way – rather than, as had been predicted, following behind a socialist Europe? Did he ever imagine that what his revolution would liberate was Russian slavery itself – that his revolution would enable Russian slavery to spread beyond the confines of Russia, to become a torch lighting a new path for humanity?

Russia was no longer drinking in the spirit of freedom from the West. Instead, the West was gazing in fascination at this Russian spectacle – of modernisation through non-freedom.

The world saw the bewitching simplicity of this path. The world saw the strength of this People's State built upon non-freedom.

The words of Russia's prophets seemed to have been fulfilled.

But they were fulfilled in the strangest and most terrible of ways.

Lenin's synthesis of non-freedom and socialism stupefied the world more than the discovery of nuclear energy.

The European apostles of national revolutions saw the flame in the East. First the Italians and then the Germans began to develop the concept of national socialism in their own ways.

And the flame kept spreading. It was taken up by Asia and Africa.

Nations and states could develop in the name of power! They could develop in contempt of freedom!

This was not nourishment for the healthy. It was a narcotic for failures, for the sick and the weak, for the backward and beaten.

Through the will, passion and genius of Lenin, Russia's thousand-year-old law of development became a worldwide law.

So history decreed.

Lenin's intolerance, his forcefulness, his intransigence in the face of disagreement, his contempt for freedom, the fanaticism of his faith, his cruelty towards his enemies – all the qualities that brought victory to his cause were born and forged in the thousand-year-old depths of Russian slavery. That is why his victory served the cause of non-freedom. And in the meantime other aspects of Lenin, the traits that have charmed millions, the traits of a kind, modest Russian working intellectual did not cease to exist – but they existed immaterially, without significance.

So. Is the Russian soul still as enigmatic as ever? No, there is no enigma.

Was there ever an enigma? What enigma can there be in slavery?

But then is this truly a specifically and uniquely Russian law of development? Can it truly be the lot of the Russian soul, and of the Russian soul alone, to evolve not with the growth of freedom but with the growth of slavery? Can this truly be the fate of the Russian soul?

No, no, of course not.

This law is determined by the parameters – and there are dozens, maybe even hundreds of such parameters – within which Russian history has unfolded.

'Soul' is neither here nor there; it simply does not come into it. If the French or the Germans, the Italians or the English, had been placed a thousand years ago within the same parameters of forest, steppe, bog and plain, in the force field between Europe and Asia, amid Russia's tragic vastness, then the pattern of their history would have been no different from that of Russian history. Anyway, it is not only the Russians who have known this path. There are many people on every continent of this earth who have come to know the bitterness of the Russian path – some only vaguely and from a distance, some closely and clearly, suffering bitterness of their own.

It is time for the students and diviners of Russia to understand that the mystique of the Russian soul is simply the result of a thousand years of slavery.

And in admiration of the Byzantine purity and Christian meekness of the Russian soul there lies an involuntary recognition of the inviolability of Russian slavery. The sources of this Christian meekness and Byzantine ascetic purity are the same as the sources of Lenin's passion, intolerance and fanatical faith – they lie in the thousand years of Russian serfdom, Russian non-freedom.

And this is why the Russian prophets were so tragically mistaken. Where, where can we find this 'Russian soul, all-human and all-unifying', that Dostoevsky told us would 'speak the final word of the great general harmony, of the final brotherly concord of all tribes according to the law of the Gospel of Christ'?

Where indeed, O Lord, is this all-human and all-unifying soul to be found? Did Russia's prophets ever imagine that their prophecies about the coming universal triumph of the Russian soul would find their grating fulfilment in the unity of the barbed wire stretched around Auschwitz and the labour camps of Siberia?

Lenin was in many ways opposed to the great prophets of Russia. He is infinitely far from their ideals of meekness, of Christian, Byzantine purity and the laws of the Gospel. But he is also strangely and surprisingly close to these prophets. While going his own very different way, he made no effort to save Russia from her thousand-year-old quagmire of non-freedom. Like them, he recognised Russian slavery as unshakeable. Like them, he was born of our non-freedom.

The Russian slave soul lives both in Russian faith and in Russian lack of faith, both in Russian meek love of humanity and in the Russian propensity to reckless violence. It lives in Russian miserliness and philistinism, in Russian obedient industriousness, in Russian ascetic purity, in the Russian capacity for fraud on a supreme scale, in the redoubtable braveness of Russian warriors, in the Russian lack of any sense of human dignity, in the frenzy of Russian sectarians and in the desperate ferocity with which Russian rebels rebel. The Russian slave soul is manifest in Lenin's revolution, in Lenin's passionate embrace of Western revolutionary teachings, in Lenin's fanaticism, in Lenin's violence and in the victories of the Leninist State.

Wherever slavery exists in the world, it gives birth to souls of the same kind.

What hope is there for Russia if even her great prophets were unable to distinguish freedom from slavery?

What hope is there for Russia if her geniuses see submissive slavery as the expression of the meek, bright beauty of her soul?

What hope is there for Russia if Lenin, the man who did most to transform her, did not destroy but only strengthened the link between Russian progress and Russian non-freedom?

When will we see the day of a free, human, Russian soul? When will this day dawn?

Or will it never dawn?

23

Lenin died. But Leninism did not die. Lenin's Party did not surrender the power that Lenin had won. Lenin's comrades, helpers and disciples continued his work.

> *The men he left behind*
> *Must bind with concrete dykes*
> *Lands overwhelmed by flood.*
> *No grief can make them pause;*
> *They don't cry, 'Lenin's died'.*
> *They execute his laws;*
> *And still more sternly carry on his cause.**

Lenin bequeathed Russia many things: the dictatorship of the Party, the Red Army, the militia, the Cheka, the campaign against illiteracy, the special educational faculties for the workers. He also left twenty-eight volumes of his *Collected Works* . . . Who, though, who among Lenin's comrades would prove best able to absorb Leninism's innermost essence and express it through his heart and mind, through his whole mode of being? Who would take up Lenin's banner and carry it further? Who would finish building the vast State whose foundations Lenin had laid? Who would lead his 'party of a new type'* from victory to victory? Who would consolidate the new order?

Would it be the brilliant, impetuous, magnificent Trotsky?

The charming Bukharin, with his talent for theory and generalisation? The ox-eyed Rykov, the practically minded statesman who most closely identified with the true interests of the people, of the workers and peasants? The well-educated, self-confident Kamenev, with his sophistication, with his grasp of affairs of state, with his ability to emerge victorious from Party conventions and their complex battles? Would it be Zinoviev, the internationally respected polemicist, with his understanding of the international workers' movement?

The character, the spirit of each of these men was in harmony with one facet or another of Lenin's character. But not with the facets that proved fundamental, not with the facets that determined the essence of the new world that was coming into being.

Fate willed it that all the aspects of Lenin's character expressed in the character of Trotsky, who was so nearly a genius – or in the characters of Bukharin, Rykov, Kamenev or Zinoviev – turned out to be seditious. They led these men to the scaffold, to their death.

These character traits, far from expressing Lenin's essence, were signs of his weakness, his eccentricity, his seditiousness, his capacity for self-delusion. The essence of the new lay elsewhere.

In the Lenin who loved the 'Appassionata' and *War and Peace*, there was, after all, something of Lunacharsky. But it was not for poor old Lunacharsky to 'execute his laws' and 'sternly carry on his cause'. Nor did history choose Trotsky, Bukharin, Rykov, Kamenev or Zinoviev to express what was innermost and most essential in Lenin.

Stalin's hatred for the Old Bolsheviks who opposed him was also a hatred for those aspects of Lenin's character that contradicted what was most essential in Lenin.

Stalin executed Lenin's closest friends and comrades-in-arms because they were all, each in his own way, hindering the realisation of what was most important – of the essence of Leninism.

Struggling against them, executing them, it was as if he were struggling against Lenin, executing Lenin. But, by doing this, he was also victoriously affirming Lenin and Leninism, raising Lenin's banner over Russia and securing it there.

24

The name of Stalin is inscribed for all eternity in the history of Russia.

By looking at Stalin, post-revolutionary Russia came to know herself.

The twenty-eight volumes of Lenin's *Collected Works* – speeches, reports, programmes, economic and philosophical studies – did not help Russia to know herself and her fate. The result of confusing Western revolution and Russian ways of life was a chaos greater than that of the Tower of Babel.

It was not only the Russian peasants and workers, not only Budyonny's cavalry and the Red Sailors, who were unable to grasp what was really happening; in this respect, Lenin himself was equally helpless. The roar of the revolutionary storm, the laws of the materialist dialectic, the logic of *Das Kapital* – these blended with the whoops of accordions, anarchist street songs like 'Little Apple' and 'The Fried Chicken',* the hum of moonshine distilleries, and the appeals of Bolshevik propagandists to Petrograd sailors and students attending the new workers' faculties, urging them to resist the poisonous heresies of Kautsky, Cunow and Hilferding.

The wild violence – the arson and rioting that gripped the entire country – brought to the surface of the Russian cauldron all the grievances that had accumulated over the centuries of serfdom.

From the romanticism of the Revolution, from the craziness of *proletkult*,* from the headiness of peasant rebellion and Green Armies fuelled on moonshine, from the fury of the Bolshevik sailors during the battle for Odessa, there emerged a new police chief – a more powerful police chief than Russia had ever seen.

The peasantry passionately aspired to be the master of the land that it ploughed. This desire, which Lenin understood and encouraged, presented a danger to the State founded by Lenin. Peasant ownership of the land was incompatible with the very existence of this State. The State therefore dealt ruthlessly with this aspiration.

In 1930 the State founded by Lenin would become the sole and indivisible owner of all the lands, forests and waters of the Soviet Union. No longer would the peasantry have the right to own ploughland.

During the years following the Revolution, however, a fog of confusion and contradiction reigned not only in docks and railway junctions, not only on the crowded roofs of trains overflowing with people, not only in the aspirations of peasants and the inflamed minds of poets. There was no less confusion in the field of revolutionary theory, in the stupefying contradictions between Lenin's crystal-clear theses and what was actually happening.

Lenin's fundamental slogan in 1917 was 'All Power to the Soviets!' It is entirely clear, however, that Lenin's soviets have never possessed any power whatsoever. They have always been of secondary importance to the Party, their function either merely administrative or entirely formal.

The young Lenin devoted all his energies to the struggle against the People's Will and the Socialist Revolutionaries; the aim of all this zealous theorising was to prove that Russia could not bypass the capitalist stage of development. But in 1917 Lenin devoted his energies to proving that Russia, bypassing capitalism and its attendant democratic freedoms, could and should take the path of proletarian revolution.

Could Lenin have imagined that by founding the Communist International and by proclaiming at its Second Congress the slogan of world revolution, 'Proletarians of the World Unite!', he was preparing the ground for an unprecedented growth of the principle of national sovereignty?

The power of State nationalism and the crazed nationalism of people deprived of freedom and of their human dignity determined the course of the twentieth century. They became the main lever, the thermonuclear warhead of a new order.

Stalin taught Russia to think straight, to put the turmoil of October and Lenin behind her. A reprimand for everyone or – as the saying has it – 'earrings for every sister'. Or, if you were deemed unworthy, your earrings were torn off you – along with your ears, if not your head.

The Bolshevik Party was destined to become the Party of a national State. This fusion of Party and State found its expression in the person of Stalin. In the mind and will of Stalin, the State expressed its own mind and will.

It appeared as if Stalin was constructing the Russian State – the State founded by Lenin – in his own image and likeness. In reality, however, it was the other way round. Stalin's image was the likeness of the Russian State – which is why he became Tsar.

Although there appear to have been times – especially towards the end of his life – when Stalin saw the State as his servant.

It was Stalin – who was both a European Marxist and an Asian despot – who gave true expression to the nature of Soviet statehood. What was embodied in Lenin was a Russian national principle; what was embodied in Stalin was a statehood that was both Russian and Soviet.

Russian statehood, engendered by Asia but dressed in European clothes, is a suprahistorical phenomenon. Its principles are universal and unshakeable, applicable to all the structures that Russia has known during the thousand years of her history. With Stalin's help, all the revolutionary categories that Lenin had seen as temporary expedients – dictatorship, terror, the suppression of bourgeois freedoms – were transformed into the essence, into the very foundation of Soviet life. Fusing with Russia's thousand-year-old tradition of non-freedom, these categories became the essential content of the Soviet State. The remaining vestiges of Social Democracy, in the meantime, were relegated to the status of stage decor, of mere external form.

Stalin united within him all the most ruthless traits of slave Russia.

In Stalin's improbable cruelty and perfidy, in his capacity for pretence and hypocrisy, in his resentfulness and vindictiveness, in his coarseness, in his humour – we see a lordly Asiatic.

In Stalin's knowledge of revolutionary doctrines, in his use of the terminology of the progressive West, in his familiarity with the works of literature and theatre dear to the Russian democratic intelligentisa, in his quotations from Gogol and Saltykov-Shchedrin, in his mastery of the subtlest and most complex conspiratorial tricks, in his amorality – we see a revolutionary in the model of Nechaev, one for whom any means are justified by the future end. But Nechaev himself would, of course, have shuddered if he had known to what extremes Joseph Stalin would take the principles of Nechaevism.

In Stalin's faith in official documents and the supremacy of police power, in his passion for medals and uniforms, in his unparalleled contempt for human dignity, in his deification of order and a rigid bureaucracy, in his readiness to kill those who have infringed some holy letter of the law and then to flout this very same law through perpetrating some act of monstrous violence – we see a police boss, a top gendarme.

Stalin was a fusion of these three figures.

And it was these three Stalins who created the Stalinist State – a State bordering both cruel, treacherous, vengeful, hypocritical Asia and enlightened, democratic, mercantile, mercenary Europe; a State in which law is simply a weapon of tyranny and in which tyranny is the law; a State whose roots reach far back into the centuries of Russian serfdom, which made slaves of the peasants, and into the centuries of the Tatar yoke, which made slaves even of those who lorded it over the peasants.

This Asiatic in kid boots, quoting Saltykov-Shchedrin, skilfully employing the vocabulary of revolution while living by the laws of tribal vengeance, brought clarity into the post-revolutionary chaos. And he expressed himself – he realised his own character – through the character of the State.

The most important principle of the State he constructed is that it is a State without freedom.

In this country, huge factories, artificial seas, canals and hydroelectric power stations do not serve people; they serve a State without freedom.

In this State a man cannot sow what he wants to sow. A man is not the master of the field on which he works; he is not the owner of the apple trees he grows or of the milk he produces. Whatever the earth bears, it bears according to the instructions of the State without freedom.

In this State not only are the national minorities deprived of their freedom but so is the Russian nation itself. Where there is no individual freedom, there can be no national freedom – since national freedom is, above all, the freedom of the individual human being.

In this State there is no such thing as society. Society is

founded on people's free intimacy and free antagonism – and in a State without freedom free intimacy and free hostility are unthinkable.

The thousand-year-old principle nurtured by the Russia of the boyars,* by Ivan the Terrible, by Peter the Great and Catherine the Great, the principle according to which Russian enlightenment, science and industrial power develop by virtue of a general increase in the degree of human non-freedom – this principle achieved its most absolute triumph under Stalin.

And it is truly astonishing that Stalin, after so totally destroying freedom, continued to be afraid of it.

Perhaps it was this fear that led Stalin to display such extraordinary hypocrisy.

Stalin's hypocrisy was a clear expression of the hypocrisy of his State. And it was expressed, first and foremost, in his demand that people play at being free. The State did not openly spit on the corpse of freedom – far from it! Instead, after the precious content – the living, radioactive inner content – of freedom and democracy had been done away with, this corpse was turned into a stuffed dummy, into a shell of words. It was like the way savages, after getting their hands on the most delicate of sextants and chronometers, use them as jewellery.

The freedom that had been done away with became an adornment of the State – but by no means a useless adornment. This dead freedom became the lead actor in a gigantically conceived piece of theatre. The State without freedom created a mock parliament; it created mock elections, mock trade unions, a mock society and a mockery of social life. In this State without freedom mock groupings of every kind – mock collective-farm administrations, mock governing boards of writers' and artists' unions, mock presidiums of district and provincial executive committees, mock bureaus and mock plenums of district, provincial and central committees of national Communist parties – held discussions and passed resolutions that had already been resolved; they took decisions that had already been taken elsewhere. Even the Presidium of the Party Central Committee was no more than theatre.

This theatre reflected Stalin's nature. And it reflected the nature of the State without freedom. That is why the State needed Stalin, a man whose character fitted him to bring out the character of the State.

What was real – *really* real, and not theatre? Who *really* took decisions – and did not merely appear to take them?

The real power was Stalin. The decisions were taken by him. But he could not, of course, personally decide every question – whether Semyonova should be granted a holiday from teaching, whether the 'Dawn' collective farm should plant peas or cabbages.

The principle of the State without freedom did, in fact, require exactly this: that Stalin should take every decision himself, without exception. This, however, was physically impossible, and so questions of secondary importance were decided by Stalin's trusted agents. And they always decided them in the same way – in the spirit of Stalin.

That indeed is why they were Stalin's agents, or the agents of his agents. The decisions taken by them had one thing in common: whether these decisions related to the construction of a hydroelectric power station in the lower reaches of the Volga or to the possibility of a milkmaid called Anyuta Feoktistova being sent on a two-month course of study, they were made in the spirit of Stalin. The spirit of Stalin and the spirit of the State were, after all, identical.

It was always easy, at any congress, meeting or briefing of any kind, to recognise the trusted agents of Stalin-and-the-State. They were people whom no one argued with; they spoke, after all, in the name of Stalin-and-the-State.

That the State without freedom always acted in the name of freedom and democracy, that the State was afraid to take a step without invoking the name of freedom and democracy, bears witness to the power of freedom. There were few people whom Stalin feared, but he feared freedom constantly; he feared it to the end of his life. After killing it, he fawned on its corpse.

It is wrong to see what happened during collectivisation and during the purges simply as a senseless expression of cruelty, simply as a senseless expression of the unlimited power possessed by a single man.

In reality, the bloodshed of 1930 and 1937 was necessary to the State. As Stalin himself said, this blood was not shed for nothing. Without it, the State would not have survived. It was non-freedom that brought about the bloodshed, in order to conquer freedom. And it all began long before, under Lenin.

It was not only in politics and public activity that freedom was overcome. Freedom was overcome everywhere, from the realm of agriculture – the peasants' loss of the right to sow freely and harvest freely – to the realms of poetry and philosophy. It is the same whether we are talking about shoemaking, the choice of reading matter, or the possibility of moving from one apartment to another; in every sphere of life, freedom was overcome. It was the same with regard to factory work: work norms, pay, safety measures – all depended on the will of the State.

From the Pacific Ocean to the Black Sea, non-freedom triumphed – everywhere and in everything. Everywhere and in everything, freedom was killed.

It was a victorious offensive, and it could never have been carried out without a great deal of bloodshed. Freedom, after all, is life; to overcome freedom, Stalin had to kill life.

Stalin's character found expression in the vast projects of the Five-Year Plans. These thundering twentieth-century pyramids corresponded to the grandiose palaces and monuments of Asiatic antiquity that so captivated his soul. Mankind had no more need of Stalin's vast constructions than God needed those vast temples and mosques.

Stalin's character found especially vivid expression in the work of the security organs he created.

Interrogations under torture; the destruction wrought by Ivan the Terrible's *oprichniki*,* who were called upon to destroy not only individuals but whole social classes; police methods introduced by Malyuta Skuratov and further developed by Count Benckendorff – all these found their equivalents in Stalin's soul, and in the work of the apparatus of repression that he created.

But a still more sinister phenomenon was the conjunction, in Stalin's soul, of the Russian revolutionary tradition with the no less Russian tradition of a powerful secret police force operating without restraint. This conjunction – which became part of Stalin's nature and was reflected in the security organs that he created – also had its historical prototype.

It is the fateful association of Degaev – an intellectual, a prominent member of the People's Will and, eventually, a double agent – with Colonel Sudeikin, head of the Tsarist Secret Police, an association that occurred when Stalin was still only a little boy, that most clearly represents this prototype.

Sudeikin was intelligent and sceptical. He knew a great deal about the power of revolutionary Russia and he was no less aware of the pathetic incompetence of his masters, the Tsar and his ministers, whom he observed with sardonic amusement. In his capacity of secret policeman, he made use of Degaev. Degaev was thus working both for the Revolution and for the secret police.

Sudeikin failed. His aim had been first to encourage the revolutionaries, then to forge false cases against them. With the help of the Revolution he would intimidate the

Tsar, seize the reins of power himself and become a dictator. Having won supreme power, he would then annihilate the Revolution. But his bold dreams were never realised – he was assassinated by Degaev.

Stalin, however, succeeded. And Stalin's triumph contained within it – somewhere hidden from everyone, somewhere hidden even from his own self – the triumph of Sudeikin's dream. Sudeikin had dreamed of harnessing two horses – revolution and the secret police – to one cart; Stalin had realised this dream.

Stalin, who had been born of the Revolution, did away with the Revolution and the revolutionaries once and for all – with the help of the secret police.

Perhaps the persecution mania that so tormented Stalin was born of fear – the same secret fear that Sudeikin had felt with regard to Degaev.

Outwardly obedient, ostensibly harnessed to the work of the Third Section, Degaev had continued to inspire terror in the police colonel. But what is far more terrifying is that both of these men – friends, enemies, mutual betrayers – remained alive in the cramped darkness of Stalin's soul.

And it is perhaps here, or hereabouts, that we can find an explanation for one of the questions that most bewildered people in 1937. Why was it necessary, in the course of destroying innocent people who were devoted to the Revolution, to elaborate detailed scenarios, false from beginning to end, of their involvement in entirely imaginary, non-existent conspiracies?

By torturing them for days, weeks, months and sometimes even whole years, the security organs compelled poor, tormented accountants, engineers and agronomists to take part in theatrical productions, to play the roles of villains, foreign agents, terrorists and saboteurs.

To what purpose? Millions of people have asked themselves this question millions of times.

Sudeikin, after all, put on his theatrical productions in order to deceive the Tsar. But Stalin did not need to deceive the Tsar; he *was* the Tsar.

Yes, yes, of course . . . But all the same, Stalin *was* trying to deceive the Tsar. He was trying, through his theatrical productions, to deceive a Tsar who, in spite of everything, against Stalin's own will, lived on in the secret dark of his soul. An invisible sovereign was still living there – an invisible sovereign was still present in all the places where non-freedom appeared to have triumphed undisputedly. Stalin was terrified of this Tsar, and of this Tsar alone, until the end of his days.

Stalin was unable, in spite of all the millions he killed, to do away with freedom. He was unable, until the end of his days, to do away with the freedom in whose name the February Revolution had flared up.

And so the Asiatic despot living in Stalin's soul tried to deceive freedom. Despairing of doing away with freedom once and for all, he tried to outwit freedom, to pull the wool over the eyes of freedom.

25

Just as Lenin's work did not die in 1924, so Stalin's work lived on after his death.

The State without freedom, the State built by Stalin, still lives. The apparatus of power – heavy industry, the armed forces, the security organs – is still in the grip of the Party. Non-freedom still reigns, unshakeable, from the Pacific Ocean to the White and the Black Seas. Theatre still penetrates every aspect of life. There is still the same system of elections; the workers' unions are as shackled as ever; the peasants are still without internal passports, without even the freedom to move; the intelligentsia of a great country – still producing talented work – is still confined to the servants' room, from where one can hear the hum of its chatter. Government is still simply a matter of issuing commands, of pressing buttons, and the power of the supreme controller is still unlimited.

Much, of course, has changed – inevitably and irrevocably.

The State without freedom has entered its third phase. It was founded by Lenin. It was constructed by Stalin. And now phase three has begun: the State, as an engineer might say, has been put into operation.

Much that was necessary during the period of construction has ceased to be necessary. The time to demolish the little old houses that happened to stand on the site of the new building has passed; the time to destroy or deport the inhabitants of all the old dwellings has passed.

The new skyscraper is inhabited by new tenants. There are, of course, still imperfections, but there is no need to go on employing the extermination methods of the late, great builder, the old boss.

The skyscraper's foundation – non-freedom – is as unshakeable as ever.

What will come next? Is this foundation really so unshakeable?

Was Hegel right? Can everything that is real really be rational? Is the inhuman real? Is the inhuman rational?

The power of the people's revolution that began in February 1917 was so great that not even the dictatorial State was able to stifle it. And while the State was proceeding, for its own sake, down its cruel and terrible path of growth and accumulation, it was, without knowing it, bearing freedom within its womb.

In deep darkness, in deep secrecy, freedom was coming to be. A river that swept away everything in its path, a river that had become the one and only reality, was thundering across the earth's surface. The new national State that was the sovereign of every living breath and the sole owner of countless treasures – of factories, of nuclear reactors, of every last field in the country – was celebrating its victory. The Revolution seemed to have taken place solely for the sake of this State, for the sake of its thousand years of triumphant power. Nevertheless, the sovereign of half the world was not simply a gravedigger of freedom.*

In spite of the genius of Lenin, the inspired creator of a new world, freedom was coming to be. In spite of Stalin's limitless, cosmic violence, freedom was coming to be. It was coming to be because human beings were still human beings.

It was man who carried out the revolution of February 1917; it was man who constructed skyscrapers, factories and nuclear reactors at the new State's command – and there is no other way for man but freedom. Because even while constructing a new world, human beings remained human beings.

Ivan Grigoryevich felt and understood all of this – sometimes clearly, sometimes vaguely.

No matter how vast the skyscrapers and powerful the cannon, no matter how limitless the power of the State, no matter how mighty the empire, all this is only mist and fog and – as such – will be blown away. Only one true force remains; only one true force continues to evolve and live; and this force is liberty. To a man, to live means to be free. No, not everything that is real is rational. Everything inhuman is senseless and useless.

It did not surprise Ivan Grigoryevich that the word 'freedom' had been on his lips when he was sent to Siberia as a young student and that this word was still alive in him, still present in his mind, even today.

26

He was alone in the room, but in his mind, in his thoughts, he was talking to Anna Sergeyevna.

'Do you know? At the very worst times I used to imagine being embraced by a woman. I used to imagine this embrace as something so wonderful that it would make me forget everything I had been through. It would be as if none of it had ever happened. But it turns out that it's you I have to talk to, that it's you I have to tell about the very worst time of all. You yourself, after all, talked all through that night. Happiness, it turns out, will be to share with you the burden I can't share with anyone else – the burden I can share only with you. When you come back from the hospital, I'll tell you about that hardest hour. It was a conversation in a prison cell, at dawn, after an interrogation. One of my cell mates – he's no longer alive, he died soon afterwards – was called Aleksey Samoilovich. I think he was the most intelligent man I've ever met. But he frightened me, I found his mind very frightening. Not because it was evil – an evil mind is not really frightening. His mind wasn't evil, but indifferent and mocking; he mocked faith. He appalled me but, more important, he also attracted me. It was as if I were being sucked in, and I could do nothing about it. I couldn't make him share my faith in freedom.

'His life had gone badly, but then there was nothing particularly special about it. It was no different from the lives of many other people. He had been accused of spreading anti-Soviet propaganda – Article 58, Section 10, the most common accusation of all.

'But he had a powerful mind. The flow of his thoughts was like a great wave. Sometimes it would sweep me away. Sometimes I would tremble, as the earth can tremble when a wave breaks.

'I was brought back to my cell after being interrogated. What a list one could make of techniques of violence: burning at the stake, prisons, today's prison fortresses the size of a provincial capital, and the labour camps themselves. The original instruments of capital punishment were a hemp rope and a club that crushed your head; nowadays, though, an executioner just turns on the master switch and does away with a hundred, or a thousand, or ten thousand people. There's no need now to raise an axe. Our age is an age of supreme violence on the part of the State – supreme violence against the individual human being. But in this lies our strength and our hope. It is the twentieth century that has shaken Hegel's principle of the rationality of the world historical process, of the rationality of everything that is real. After decades of troubled debate, nineteenth-century Russian thinkers came to accept this principle, but now, at the height of the State's triumph over human freedom, Russian thinkers in padded camp jackets are overturning Hegel's principle and proclaiming *this* supreme principle of universal history: "All that is inhuman is senseless and useless."

'Yes, yes, yes, at this time of the total triumph of in-humanity it has become clear that everything created by violence is senseless and useless. It exists without a future; it will leave no trace.

'This is my faith, and with it I returned to my cell. And Aleksey Samoilovich said, as he often did, "Why try to defend freedom? Long ago it was indeed seen as the law of progress, the meaning of progress. Now, however, it's entirely clear that there is no such thing as historical evolution. History is simply a molecular process. Man is simply man, and there is nothing that can be done with him. There is no evolution. There is one very simple law, the law of the conservation of violence. It's as simple as the law of the conservation of energy. Violence is eternal, no matter what is done to destroy it. It does not disappear or diminish; it can only change shape. It can be embodied in slavery, or in the Mongol invasion. It migrates from continent to continent. Sometimes it takes the form of class struggle, sometimes of race struggle. From the sphere of the material it slips into religiosity, as in the Middle Ages. Sometimes it is directed against coloured people, sometimes against writers and artists, but, all in all, the total quantity of violence on earth remains constant. Thinkers mistake its constant chaotic transformations for evolution and search for its laws. But chaos knows no laws, no evolution, no meaning and no aim. Gogol, our Russian genius, sang of a flying troika – and in the flight of this troika he saw Russia's future. Russia's future, however, turned out to lie not in Gogol's troika of horses, but in our faceless Soviet troikas: in the NKVD troikas that sentence men to be shot, in the village troikas that compiled lists of kulaks, in the troikas that expelled young people from universities, in the troikas that denied ration cards to an old woman they considered a 'former' person."

'There this man was, sitting on the bed boards, shaking an admonitory finger at Gogol: "You got it wrong, Nikolay Vasilyevich, you didn't understand our Russian troika, you didn't see it clearly enough. Human history is not a matter of flying troikas but of chaos, of the eternal transformation of one kind of violence into another. The troika flies, but everything round about is motionless and frozen. Man, above all, is motionless; his fate is motionless. Violence is eternal, no matter what is done to destroy it. And the troika flies on – and what does it care about Russian grief? And what does Russian grief care about the troika? What does Russian grief care whether the troika is flying or whether it's come to a standstill?

'"And in any case it's not Gogol's troika signing death warrants somewhere here in this building but our very own troika – our very own NKVD troika."

'And I'm lying half dead on the bed boards, and the only thing alive in me is my faith: my belief that human history is the history of freedom, of the movement from less freedom to more freedom; my belief that the history of life – from the amoeba to the human race – is the history of freedom, of the movement from less freedom to more freedom; my belief that life itself is freedom. And this faith gives me strength, and I keep turning over in my mind a precious, luminous and wonderful thought that has been hidden in our prison rags. As if with my hands, I keep exploring this thought: "All that is inhuman is senseless and useless."

'Aleksey Samoilovich hears me out, half alive as I am, and says, "That's just a comforting lie. The history of life is the history of violence triumphant. Violence is eternal and inde-structible. It can change shape, but it does not disappear or diminish. Even the word 'history', even the concept of history is just something people have dreamed up. There's no such thing as history. History is milling the wind; history is grinding water with a pestle and mortar. Man does not evolve from lower to higher. Man is as motionless as a slab of granite. His goodness, his intelligence, his degree of freedom are motionless; the humanity in humanity does not increase. What history of humanity can there be if man's goodness always stands still?"

'And, you know, it felt as if nothing in the world could

be worse than all this. I'm lying on the bed boards and, dear God, I start to feel an anguish that is more than I can bear – all from talking to one very clever man. It feels like death, like an execution. Even breathing feels more than I can bear. I want only one thing: not to see, not to hear, not to breathe. To die. But relief came from a quite unexpected quarter. I was dragged off again to be interrogated. They didn't give me time to get my breath back. And I felt better, I felt relieved. Freedom, I knew again, is inevitable. To hell with troikas that fly, thunder and sign death warrants. Freedom and Russia will be united!

'You can't hear me. When will you come back to me from the hospital?'

On a winter's day Ivan Grigoryevich accompanied Anna Sergeyevna to the cemetery. He did not have the chance to share with her all that he had recalled, all that he had thought through, all that he had noted down during the months of her illness.

He took all her things to the village, spent a day with Alyosha and returned to the workshop.

27

In the summer Ivan Grigoryevich travelled to the seaside town where, beneath a green hill, his father's house had stood.

The train went right along the shore. During a short stop, Ivan Grigoryevich got out and looked at the green-and-black water. It was always moving, and it smelled cool and salty.

The wind and the sea had been there when the investigator summoned him for interrogations during the night. They had been there while a grave was being dug for a prisoner who had died in transit. They had been there while guard dogs barked beneath the barrack windows and the snow creaked beneath the guards' boots.

The sea was eternal, and the eternity of its freedom seemed to Ivan Grigoryevich to be akin to indifference. The sea had not cared about Ivan Grigoryevich when he was living beyond the Arctic Circle, nor would its thundering, splashing freedom care about him when he ceased to live. No, he thought, this is not freedom. This is astronomical space come down to earth, a splinter of eternity, indifferent, always in motion.

The sea was not freedom; it was a likeness of freedom, a symbol of freedom . . . How splendid freedom must be if a mere likeness of it, a mere reminder of it, is enough to fill a man with happiness.

After passing the night in the station, he set off early in

the morning towards the house. An autumn sun was rising in a cloudless sky, and it was impossible to distinguish it from a spring sun.

The silence around him was deserted and sleepy. He felt such an intensity of emotion that it seemed as if his heart, which had endured everything, would be unable to endure it. The world became divinely still; the dear sanctuary of his childhood was eternal and immutable. His feet had long ago trodden these cool cobbles; his child's eyes had gazed at these rounded hills now touched by the red rust of autumn. He listened to the noise of the stream, on its way to the sea amid watermelon rinds, gnawed corncobs and other town detritus.

An old Abkhazian man, wearing a black sateen shirt girded by a thin leather belt, was carrying a basket of chestnuts towards the bazaar.

Ivan Grigoryevich might perhaps, in his childhood, have bought figs and chestnuts from this same unchanging old greybeard. And it was the same southern morning air – both cool and warm, smelling of the sea and of the mountain sky, of roses and of garlic from the kitchens. And the same little houses with closed shutters and drawn curtains. And behind these shutters were sleeping the same children – children who had never grown up – and the same old men as forty years ago – still not gone to their graves.

He came out onto the main road and began to climb the hill. There was the sound of the stream again. Ivan Grigoryevich could remember its voice.

Never before had he seen his life as a whole – but now here it was, lying before him.

And, seeing his life, he felt no resentment towards anyone.

All of them – those who had prodded him with their rifle butts as they escorted him towards the investigator's office, those who had subjected him to long interrogations without letting him sleep, those who had said vile things about him at public meetings, those who had officially renounced him, those who had stolen his camp ration of bread, those who had beaten him – all of them, in their weakness, coarseness and spite had done evil without wanting to. They had not wanted to do evil to him.

They had betrayed, slandered and renounced because there had been no other way for them to survive. And yet they were people; they were human beings. Had these people wanted him to be making his way like this to his abandoned home – old, alone and without love?

People did not want to do evil to anyone, but they did evil throughout their lives.

All the same, people were people, they were human beings. And the wonderful, marvellous thing is that, willingly or unwillingly, they did not allow freedom to die. In their terrible, distorted, yet still-human souls, even the most terrible of them looked after freedom and kept it alive.

He had achieved nothing. He would leave behind him no books, no paintings, no discoveries. He had created no school of thought, no political party, and he had no disciples.

Why had his life been so hard? He had not preached; he had not taught; he had simply remained what he had been since birth – a human being.

The mountainside opened out before him. From the other side of the pass appeared the tops of oak trees. He had walked there as a child, searching in the half-dark of the forest for traces of the Circassians and their vanished way of life: fruit trees gone wild, remnants of what had once been a fence round a house.

Perhaps his own home would still be as unchanged as the town streets and the stream?

It would be at the next turn of the road. For a moment it seemed to him as if an improbably bright light, brighter than any light he had ever seen, had flooded the whole earth.

A few more steps – and in this light he would see his home, and his mother would come out towards him, towards her prodigal son, and he would kneel down before her, and her young and beautiful hands would rest on his grey, balding head.

He saw thickets of thorns and hops. There was no house and no well – only a few stones shining white amid dusty grass that had been burned by the sun.

Here he stood – grey-haired, stoop-shouldered, yet still the same as ever, unchanged.

1955–63

Notes

2   *All-Union Central Council of Trade Unions*: By far the largest public organisation in the Soviet Union, this served as an umbrella organisation for the various individual trade unions.

3   *did all the ploughing*: An allusion to a proverbial fly who has been sitting for some time on the horn of an ox. When another fly asks him where he has been, he replies, 'We've been ploughing!'

4   *makhorka*: The very coarsest, strongest tobacco.

5   *first among equals*: During the nineteenth century these words were used with regard to the relationship between Russians and other Slav nationalities, especially Serbs. During and after the 1930s they were applied, semi-officially, to the relationship between Russians and other Soviet nationalities.

9   *Vanya*: The most common affectionate form of Ivan.

14   *candidate's dissertation*: A *kandidatskaya dissertatsiya* is the equivalent of a PhD. A *doktorskaya dissertatsiya*, here translated as 'doctorate', is an even higher degree.

15   *vitalism*: This is the doctrine that the functioning of a living organism is determined by a vital principle distinct from physico-chemical forces. Such a way of thinking was, of course, unacceptable to the guardians of the 'scientific materialism' that was the Soviet orthodoxy.

18   *Killer Doctors*: On 13 January 1953, some of the most prominent doctors in the USSR were accused of taking part in a vast plot to poison members of the political and military

leadership. *Pravda* reported the accusations under the headline VICIOUS SPIES AND KILLERS PASSING THEMSELVES OFF AS DOCTORS AND PROFESSORS. Stalin evidently intended these accusations to serve as a prelude to a vast purge of Jews. Only Stalin's death, on 5 March 1953, prevented this purge from being carried out. The preparations for the affair of the Killer Doctors began at least a year in advance. Early in 1952, after the death in Moscow of the Mongolian dictator Marshal Choibalsan, Stalin said, 'They die one after another. Shcherbakov, Zhdanov, Dimitrov, Choibalsan . . . die so quickly! We must change the old doctors for new ones.' Later that year, perhaps in response to this remark, Mikhail Ryumin, deputy minister for state security, alleged that the Jewish professor Yakov Etinger had, under the pretence of treating Zhdanov and Shcherbakov, set out to kill them. When his superior refused to believe the story, Ryumin went over his head directly to Stalin, who immediately suspected a wider conspiracy to kill off the Soviet leadership.

21   *Stalin's Short Course*: *The Short Course of the History of the All-Russian Communist Party (Bolshevik)* was published in 1938. Between then and 1953, more than 42 million copies of the book were issued in sixty-seven languages. Most often referred to simply as *The Short Course*, it was seen as the encyclopedia of Marxism; it is notable for the frequency with which Lenin and Stalin are repeatedly mentioned in the same phrase, as if the two names were inseparable. Stalin supervised and heavily edited the work but himself contributed only one section of Chapter 4, about dialectical and historical materialism. After the Second World War, however, he claimed sole authorship.

22   *All-Union Society for Cultural Ties with Foreign Countries*: The organisation, founded in 1925, was responsible for all cultural and scientific exchanges and contacts with other countries.

27   *Khodynka*: A mass panic occurred on Khodynka Field in north-west Moscow during festivities following the coronation of

Nicholas II, the last Russian Tsar. This resulted, according to official sources, in the death of 1,389 people.

29 *the scroll of his life*: Grossman is alluding to a line from a short poem by Pushkin, 'Memory' (1828): 'Memory silently unrolls before me its long scroll.'

30 *Lubyanka*: A large square in central Moscow where the headquarters of Soviet state security (regardless of its many changes of name) has been located since 1920. Like all headquarters buildings of the Soviet state security organisations, it contained an internal pre-trial prison, invisible from outside.

30 *Moscow Trials*: A series of show trials of real and imagined political opponents of Stalin. The first trial, of Grigory Zinoviev, Lev Kamenev and fourteen other Left Deviationists, was held in August 1936; all the defendants were sentenced to death. The second trial, in January 1937, was of seventeen lesser figures; thirteen were shot and the remaining four sent to labour camps. The third trial, in March 1938, was of Nikolay Bukharin, former head of the Communist International; Aleksey Rykov, a former prime minister; and nineteen other Right Deviationists. All the leading defendants were executed. Andrey Vyshinsky was the chief prosecutor at all three trials. The most terrible year of Stalin's purges has always been seen as 1937, and this may have led Grossman to forget that the trial of Bukharin and Rykov was in fact held in early 1938.

31 *weekly parcel of food*: The pay differential between members of the Soviet elite and ordinary workers was less than in most societies. For the main part, the elite received their payments in kind. One of their many privileges was to be provided regularly with food that it was impossible to obtain in ordinary shops.

31 *War Communism*: The economic and political system that existed in Soviet Russia from 1918 to 1921. All industry was nationalised; all private enterprise was illegal; workers were

shot for going on strike; grain and other products were requisitioned from the peasants for centralised distribution among the remaining population. The requisitioning of grain led to what was, in effect, a second civil war: the peasants grew less and less grain, and the Bolsheviks resorted to ever increasing violence in order to extort from the peasants what little grain they had grown. Together with the severe drought of 1921, this war between city and country resulted in a serious famine and the death of three to ten million peasants. After an uprising in March 1921 by sailors at the naval base of Kronstadt, Lenin made a tactical retreat, introducing the relatively liberal New Economic Policy, which lasted until 1928.

33   *Higher Academic Council*: The panel of scientists then responsible, on behalf of the Academy of Sciences, for making decisions on appointments and higher degrees.

39   *'Indians'*: A disciplinary barracks was often referred to as 'India', probably because it was often surprisingly hot. Jacques Rossi, who spent time in the Gulag, writes: 'A crowded barracks is hot, like in India, even during winter, and virtually everyone is half-naked. Some are hot and others have lost all their clothes in card games.' (*The Gulag Handbook* [New York: Paragon House, 1989], 141.)

39   *the 'thieves' and the 'bitches'*: Russian criminals were in a position of considerable power in the camps, and they lorded it over the political prisoners. They referred to themselves as 'thieves' and strictly observed a so-called thieves' code (*vorovskoy zakon*) which, among other things, forbade any collaboration with the authorities. Thieves who violated this code and collaborated with the authorities were known as 'bitches'.

39   *'engineer-saboteurs'*: The first important show trial in Stalin's Soviet Union was the Shakhty Trial in 1928. A group of engineers in the north Caucasus town of Shakhty was accused of conspiring, with foreign support, to sabotage the Soviet economy. This marked the beginning of the use

of accusations of sabotage – an accusation made more and more often during the 1930s.

39   *six-month city passport*: From late 1932 until the 1960s, collective-farm workers did not have the right to an internal passport. This meant that they had little more freedom of movement than they had had as serfs.

40   He washed the old man's feet: From 'The Grandfather' (1870) by Nikolay Nekrasov. The grandfather is one of the Decembrist rebels who, hoping to install a constitutional monarchy, took part in a failed coup against Nicholas I in December 1825. Like Ivan Grigoryevich, the grandfather has just returned from years of exile and forced labour in Siberia.

42   *'without right of correspondence'*: During the purges, when a prisoner was executed, his relatives were usually told that he was being sentenced to 'ten years without right of correspondence'.

44   *realm of form . . . realm of content*: A key Stalinist axiom was that culture should be 'national in form and Socialist in content'. Nikolay Andreyevich is – very perceptively – pointing out that this principle has been superseded.

44   *Black Hundreds*: A reactionary, militantly anti-Semitic movement in Russia in the early twentieth century.

48   *'hard-class'*: Ivan is travelling the cheapest possible way. A 'hard-class' carriage is not divided into compartments. The berths are in two tiers, on either side of a narrow corridor.

49   *Circassia*: Circassia once comprised a large area around the north-east coast of the Black Sea and the north-west of the Caucasus; the traditional inhabitants, the Circassians, prefer to be called the *Adyghe* or *Adiga*. Once part of the Ottoman empire, Circassia was gradually conquered by Russia in a series of brutal wars between 1763 and 1864. These wars ended with the majority of the population either trying to escape or else being deported – either to the Ottoman Empire or to parts of the Russian empire far from their home territories. Huge numbers died in now-forgotten refugee camps

231

on the Turkish coast. Estimates vary greatly, but it is likely that at least half the Circassian population of two million died. This genocide has been almost entirely neglected by both Western and Russian historians. Grossman is one of very few Russians even to have touched on it.

54 *the Siege*: The Siege of Leningrad lasted from September 1941 to January 1943, when a narrow land corridor to the city was established. The Siege, however, was not totally lifted until January 1944; it was one of the longest and most destructive sieges in history.

56 *shared with two chance companions*: It was customary for drunks to gather in threesomes in alcohol shops, pay for a bottle of vodka together, and then share it on a park bench or in the main entrance of some nearby building.

57 *laurel-crowned horseman*: *The Bronze Horseman* is the usual name for a famous equestrian statue of Peter the Great, unveiled in 1782. Peter the Great sits heroically on horseback, his arm pointing towards the River Neva; his horse, rearing at the edge of a cliff, is trampling a serpent under its back hooves. *The Bronze Horseman* is also the title of one of Aleksandr Pushkin's masterpieces, a narrative poem written fifty years later, in 1833. The hero of this poem is Yevgeny, a young clerk whose sweetheart is drowned when the Neva overflows its banks. Yevgeny shakes his fist at *The Bronze Horseman* and curses Peter the Great for founding the city somewhere so vulnerable to flooding. The statue comes alive and chases Yevgeny through the city. The poem's central theme is the conflict between the needs of the State and the needs of ordinary citizens.

58 *I have a passport*: That is, an 'internal passport', which Ivan Grigoryevich would have received on his release.

61 *classified as a kulak*: Peasants were classified as poor peasants (*bednyaki*), who had no property of their own; middle peasants (*serednyaki*), who owned property but did not employ hired labour; and rich peasants, or kulaks, who both owned

property and employed hired labour. During collectivisation, the kulaks were deported en masse. According to data from Soviet archives, more than 1.8 million kulaks and family members were deported in 1930 and 1931; nearly 500,000 of these appear to have died or escaped before reaching the camps or labour colonies that were their destination. Nearly 400,000 kulaks and family members are said to have died between 1932 and 1940.

71 *'Push that which is falling'*: A sarcastic allusion to Nietzsche: 'But I say: what is falling, we should still push! Everything today – it is falling, it is falling apart: who would hold it up? but I – I would still push it . . .' (*Thus Spake Zarathustra*, translated by Thomas Wayne [New York: Algora Publishing, 2003], 161.)

72 *stand 'almost side by side'*. The learned informer is quoting a famous line of the Futurist poet Vladimir Vladimirovich Mayakovsky (1893–1930). In his 'Jubilee Poem' written for the 125th anniversary of Pushkin's birth, Mayakovsky declares that, since his own name begins with *M* and Pushkin's with *P*, he and Pushkin will, in the eyes of posterity, be standing 'almost side by side'.

75 *the word 'Man'*: In the last act of Maksim Gorky's play *The Lower Depths*, Satin says: 'M-A-N! That is magnificent! That has a . . . proud sound! We must respect man! Not pity him . . . not humiliate him with pity. We must respect him!'

76 *Intourist*: Throughout the Soviet Union all hotels, restaurants, and other facilities for tourists were managed by Intourist. Intourist restaurants were, on the whole, superior to other restaurants, and they were open only to foreigners and to members of the Soviet elite. *Inturist* is a contraction of *inostrannyi turist* – 'foreign tourist'.

80 *Tsarskoye Selo*: The small town outside Petersburg that, from the late eighteenth century, was the main summer residence of the Russian tsars.

82   *application for a pension*: Soviet soldiers or officers taken prisoner by the Germans were considered suspect. Most of them
were sent to the camps on their return to the Soviet Union.
Widows only received pensions if there was documented
evidence that their husbands had died on the battlefield. The
Soviet defeats of the first months of the war were so swift,
and so catastrophic, that such evidence was seldom recorded.

82   *footcloths*: These were lengths of cloth wound around the
foot and ankle. Throughout the nineteenth and early twentieth centuries these were far more common in Russia than
socks or stockings. By the 1950s, however, they had become
less common, though still used in the army and in the camps.

84   *Putilov Factory*: By 1917, this factory, which produced both
artillery and rolling stock for the railways, was the largest in
Petrograd. It had strong revolutionary traditions; a strike there
in February 1917 was part of the chain of events that led to the
February Revolution and the Tsar's abdication. After the October
Revolution it produced the first Soviet tractors; after the assassination of Kirov in 1934, it was renamed the Kirov Factory.

84   *sentenced under Article 58*: That is, as a counter-revolutionary.

86   *labour day*: A labour day is the equivalent of the average
amount of work that – supposedly – could be performed
by one person in the course of a working day. This amount
of work – for example, ploughing a hectare of land or
threshing a ton of grain – would often, in fact, take several
days to carry out. At the end of the season the income of
the collective farm in money and kind was shared according
to the number of labour days each member had to his credit.
(Robert Conquest, *The Harvest of Sorrow* [New York: Oxford
University Press, 1986], 176–7.)

88   *a cook can govern the State*: Lenin was popularly believed to
have said, 'Every cook must learn to govern the state' or even
'Every cook can govern the state.' What Lenin in fact wrote,
in an article published in 1917, 'Will the Bolsheviks Retain

Government Power?', is more or less the opposite: 'We know that an unskilled labourer or a cook cannot immediately get on with the job of state administration.'

91 *That's something I should have done thirty years ago*: Ivan Grigoryevich is, in many respects, a portrait of the real-life Nikolay Mikhailovich Sochevets, the brother of Vasily Grossman's second wife. Nikolay Mikhailovich's father was a gifted and successful agronomist. He built himself a house near Sochi and lived there until Total Collectivisation, when he and his large family were deported to Siberia. Nikolay Mikhailovich's parents and three of his sisters all died in exile, but he himself not only survived but even completed a course in accounting and was so successful in his subsequent work that he received a so-called 'Excellent Economist' award. This allowed him to return to Moscow in the mid-1950s. There he lived first with his elder sister Maria Mikhailovna, and later in a room in a communal flat allocated him by the factory where he was the chief accountant. During the Soviet period he exchanged this small room for an apartment near Sochi, and he and his wife used to spend their summers there. In 1990 his wife also sold her Moscow apartment, and the couple moved to Sochi permanently. Like Ivan Grigoryevich, Nikolay Mikhailovich had a gift for modelling animals; Fyodor Guber remembers him visiting Grossman most Sundays, along with other friends, and spending most of the day moulding animals from plasticine. Like Ivan Grigoryevich, Nikolay Mikhailovich discovered this gift as a result of his friendship with a young boy – Sasha, the grandson of his elder sister. Like Ivan Grigoryevich, he had a fine knowledge of history, despite having been arrested before finishing school. His grand-niece, Elena Fyodorovna Guber, remembers him as a man of great vitality, someone who was free of bitterness and who knew how to enjoy life. Fyodor Guber remembers Nikolay Mikhailovich as one of the friends who most regularly came to visit Grossman during his final

illness. (Fyodor Guber, *Pamyat' i pis'ma* [Moscow: Probel-2000, 2007] 111–12, and *Voprosy literatury* [1966, May–June, 289–90]; also personal conversation with Elyena Fyodorovna Guber and personal correspondence with Fyodor Guber.)

91   *quick-witted Newtons*: In his 'Ode on the Anniversary of the Accession to the Throne of the Empress Elizaveta Petrovna' (1747), the poet Mikhail Lomonosov expresses the hope that the Russian Earth will give birth to 'her own Platos and quick-witted Newtons'.

94   *zeks*: People sentenced to a term in a labour camp were known as *zeks*, an abbreviated form of the word *zaklyuchenny*, meaning 'someone who has been confined'.

97   '*Greens*': Participants in a peasant rebellion in the Tambov Province under the leadership of Aleksandr Antonov, a Socialist Revolutionary. At the rebellion's peak in late 1920, the Green Army numbered as many as 50,000.

99   *a vast world with its own language*: The best dictionary of camp language, Jacques Rossi's *The Gulag Handbook*, runs to 610 pages.

100   *everything flows, everything changes*: The aphorism 'Everything flows' (Πάντα ῥεῖ – *panta rhei*), chosen by Grossman as the title of this novel, has often, though probably wrongly, been attributed to Heraclitus, a pre-Socratic philosopher who lived *c*.535–*c*.475 BCE. Heraclitus considered change as central to the universe. One of his best-known aphorisms is 'You can not step twice into the same river.'

104   *even under armed guard*: Grossman wrote *Everything Flows* at a time when there was almost no reliable published information on such topics as the Gulag, Collectivisation and the Terror Famine. Given his dependence on oral sources, it is remarkable how little he has got wrong. Here, however, he seems to have been seduced by legend. There are references in Gulag memoirs to small groups of predatory female criminal convicts, and to men in some camps not seeing a

236

woman for years, but I know of no other reference to camps where men never set foot.

104   *chifir*: This is an ultra-strong tea (about fifty grams of tea per cup, and boiled rather than brewed). This was used as a narcotic and was greatly prized by the camp criminals.

105   *dreamed up*: Cf: 'In the Kengir special camp, there were prisoners [. . .] who developed elaborate relationships with people they had never met. Some actually married one another across the wall that divided the men's and women's camps, without ever meeting in person. The woman stood on one side, the man on the other; vows were said, and a prisoner priest recorded the ceremony on a piece of paper. (Anne Applebaum, *Gulag: A History of the Soviet Camps* [New York: Doubleday, 2003], 317.)

107   *Butyrka*: A pre-trial investigative prison, the largest prison in Moscow. At the height of the purges around 20,000 prisoners were kept there.

107   *'58–6–12'*: He had been sentenced under Article 58, Sections 6 and 12. Article 58 of the Soviet Criminal Code related to 'counter-revolutionary activity' in general, Section 6 to 'espionage' and Section 12 to 'failure to report counter-revolutionary activity'.

111   *Arbat*: The name of an important street in central Moscow, and also of the fashionable, bohemian quarter around this street.

114   *Mukha*: Clearly a nickname. The word means 'a fly'.

118   *camp barracks*: It is likely that much of Grossman's information about women in the Gulag came from the philosopher Tatyana Nikolaevna Gornstein. Like Grossman, she was born in Berdichev. Arrested in 1937, she survived the camps thanks to her 'privileged' work as a nurse in a camp hospital. She was released soon after Stalin's death. Tatyana Menaker, a second cousin of Grossman, remembers Gornshtein telling her about 'the mathematicians, poets and philosophers who had begged her to preserve their manuscripts as they lay on

camp beds dying from scurvy, diarrhoea and dysentery'. (Personal correspondence from Tatyana Menaker.)

120   *Magadan*: The capital of Kolyma Province, an area of north-eastern Siberia that was, in effect, one vast labour camp.

125   *special settlements*: 'The liquidation of the kulak as a class – dekulakization for short – was an integral component of collectivization and vital to its realization. Dekulakization was Stalin's first Great Purge. It was a purge of the countryside: an endeavor to remove undesirable elements and to decapitate traditional village leadership and authority structures in order to break down village cohesion, minimize peasant resistance to collectivization, and intimidate the mass of the peasantry into compliance.' (Lynne Viola, *The Unknown Gulag* [New York: Oxford University Press, 2007], 7.) Special settlements were not – legally – a form of imprisonment, but they were under the direct control of the OGPU. They were often just areas of uninhabited forest where kulaks were dumped and told to build shelter for themselves. From 1933 their importance diminished as the importance of the network of labour camps increased.

129   *we are all human beings*: Robert Conquest writes, 'The Party's . . . rationale for everything done to the kulaks is summarized with exceptional frankness in a novel [by Ilya Ehrenburg] published in Moscow in 1934: "Not one of them was guilty of anything; but they belonged to a class that was guilty of everything."' (*The Harvest of Sorrow*, 143.)

131   *all their pay went into special books*: They were therefore only able to spend their pay in particular shops.

132   *'Dizziness from Success'*: On 2 March 1930, Stalin published in *Pravda* an important article, 'Dizziness from Success', that marked a partial and temporary retreat on his part.

134   *they dug up vegetable gardens*: Robert Conquest writes, 'Their technique consisted of beating people up and of using specially issued tools – steel rods about five-eighths of an inch in diameter and from three to ten feet long, with a handle at one end

and a sharp point – or a sort of drill – at the other, to probe for grain.' (*The Harvest of Sorrow*, 229.) And Conquest quotes from a memoir by a former activist, Lev Kopelev: 'I took part in this myself, scouring the countryside, searching for hidden grain, testing the earth with an iron rod for loose spots that might lead to buried grain. With the others, I emptied out the old folks' storage chests, stopping my ears to the children's crying and the women's wails. For I was convinced that I was accomplishing a great and necessary transformation of the countryside; that in the days to come the people who lived there would be better off for it.' (*The Harvest of Sorrow*, 233.)

135 *subkulak parasites*: Peasants who were considered hostile to collectivisation, but who were too poor to be considered kulaks, were labelled 'subkulaks'.

142 *one big show*: Grossman is alluding to a visit made to the Ukraine in late summer of 1933 by the French radical leader Edouard Herriot. Conquest quotes the following account of the preparations made to receive Herriot at a collective farm near Kiev: 'A special meeting of the regional party organization was held in Kiev for the purpose of transforming this collective farm into a "Potemkin village" . . . experienced agronomists were made into brigade members of the farm . . . Furniture from the regional theatre in Brovary was brought, and the clubrooms beautifully appointed with it. Curtains and drapes were brought from Kiev, also tablecloths. One wing was turned into a dining-hall, the tables of which were covered with new cloths and decorated with flowers. The regional telephone exchange, and the switchboard operator, were transferred from Brovary to the farm. Some steers and hogs were slaughtered to provide plenty of meat. A supply of beer was also brought in. All the corpses and starving peasants were removed from the highways in the surrounding countryside and the peasants were forbidden to leave their houses. A mass meeting of collective farm workers was called, and they were told that a motion picture would be

made of collective farm life, and for this purpose this particular farm had been chosen by a film-studio from Odessa. Only those who were chosen to play in the picture would turn out for work, the rest of the members must stay at home and not interfere.' (*The Harvest of Sorrow*, 314–15.) Not all foreigners, however, were duped. As Malcolm Muggeridge reported in the early summer of 1933: 'On a recent visit to the Northern Caucasus and the Ukraine, I saw something of the battle that is going on between the government and the peasants. The battlefield is as desolate as in any war and stretches wider; stretches over a large part of Russia. On the one side, millions of starving peasants, their bodies often swollen from lack of food; on the other, soldier members of the GPU carrying out the instructions of the dictatorship of the proletariat. They had gone over the country like a swarm of locusts and taken away everything edible; they had shot or exiled thousands of peasants, sometimes whole villages; they had reduced some of the most fertile land in the world to a melancholy desert.' (Quoted in *The Harvest of Sorrow*, 260.)

143   *on the stove*: A Russian stove was a large brick or clay structure taking up between one-fifth and one-quarter of the room it stood in. Sleeping places were often arranged in relation to it. Sometimes a sleeping bench was attached to one side of it; sometimes people slept on a wide shelf above it; often people slept directly on the warm brick surface of the stove itself.

143   *taken off to the town*: 'Of a Ukrainian farm population of between twenty and twenty-five million, about five million died – a quarter to a fifth. The casualty rate varied considerably by area and even village, from 10 per cent to 100 per cent . . . Time after time, officials tell of entering villages with few or no survivors, and seeing the dead in their houses. In villages of 3,000–4,000 people . . . only 45–80 were left.' (Conquest, *The Harvest of Sorrow*, 249–51.) Tim Snyder's estimate for the number of deaths in the Ukraine

is three and a half million. ('The Real, Ignored Holocaust' in The *New York Review of Books*, 16 July 2009.)

144   *chalked on your back*: The translator and editor Natasha Perova has written of the queues she remembers from her own post-war childhood: 'There were activists who supervised the queue and wrote numbers on your palm with an indelible pencil. There were also roll calls from time to time. Sometimes someone's number would get erased accidentally. That was a tragedy. Then they started writing numbers on people's arms or elbows to keep them safe. In some queues they chalked numbers on backs to prevent cheating, but that was rare.' (Personal correspondence.)

144   *people stripped of their civic rights*: That is, those who had been designated as belonging to the category of citizens 'deprived of rights which they have used to the detriment of the Socialist Revolution'.

151   *bread rings*: Similar to Italian breadsticks, but in the shape of small rings.

160   *Lefortovo*: An important Moscow pre-trial prison. In the late 1930s it was notorious for the tortures carried out there. During these years, the corridors and cells were painted black.

161   *numerus clausus*: An 1887 decree limiting the number of Jews allowed to study in Russian universities. The proportion of Jewish students was limited to 10 per cent in cities where Jews had the right to live, 5 per cent in other cities, and 3 per cent in Moscow and St Petersburg. These restrictions were removed after the 1917 Revolution.

161   *Pale of Settlement*: The area along Russia's western border in which Jews were allowed to live. Comprising around 20 per cent of the territory of European Russia, the Pale existed from 1791 until 1917 and included much of present-day Lithuania, Belarus, Poland, Moldova and Ukraine, as well as parts of western Russia. Jews were, with certain exceptions, forbidden to live elsewhere in the Russian Empire.

161　*district and provincial . . . SovNarKhozes*: That is, of district-level and provincial-level security organs; of Revolutionary Committees, Regional Committees and Provincial Provisions and Foodstuffs Committees; of Committees of the Poor, Political Enlightenment Organisations and Soviets for the National Economy.

165　*Socialism in One Country*: This theory – that it was no longer necessary to encourage revolution in the capitalist countries, since Russia could and should achieve socialism alone – was first articulated in 1924 by Bukharin. It was then taken up by Stalin.

168　*Moscow Tailoring Combine*: Clothes produced by this factory were notoriously ugly. The poet Osip Mandelstam declared ironically during the 1930s, 'I am a man of the epoch of the Moscow Tailoring Combine.'

169　'*Golden Library*' . . . *Louis Boussenard*: The Golden Library was a famous series of classics for young people, published in the late nineteenth and early twentieth centuries; Louis Boussenard (1847–1911) wrote popular adventure novels somewhat in the manner of Jules Verne.

169　*Talmud Torah schools*: A form of primary school, dating back to the first century of the Common Era, for Jewish boys of modest backgrounds. They were given an elementary education in Hebrew, the Torah and the Talmud.

172　*everything is real and rational*: An allusion to Hegel's famous dictum, much discussed in Russian radical circles during the nineteenth century, that 'everything that is rational is real and everything that is real is rational'.

174　*voluntary working Saturdays*: There was a tradition in the Soviet Union of voluntary working Saturdays (*subbotniki*). Lenin himself participated in the first all-Russian *subbotnik* (1 May 1920), helping to remove building rubble from the Kremlin. These voluntary working Saturdays soon ceased to be voluntary – if ever they were.

174   *set Russia on a new path*: During the June 1917 Congress of
       Soviets in Petrograd, the Menshevik minister Irakli Tsereteli
       said that Russia could achieve democracy and victory in the
       war only if the different political parties cooperated. To his
       assertion that there was no single party that could take
       power and maintain order in Russia, Lenin famously declared
       from the back of the hall, 'There is such a party. It is the
       Bolshevik Party!' To most of those present, Lenin's state-
       ment seemed absurd. The Bolsheviks had 105 delegates; the
       other parties, between them, had 822.

178   *listened to the 'Appassionata'*: Lenin said that he once wept
       after listening to Beethoven's 'Appassionata' sonata. He
       famously went on to say that 'a revolutionary cannot afford
       to give way to such sentiments, because they make him too
       weak, wanting to pat his enemies on the head instead of
       fighting them mercilessly'. (Slavoj Zizek, *Revolution at the
       Gates* [London: Verso, 2002], 197.)

179   *Lenin's unfinished portrait*: The lines Grossman quotes are
       from a once well-known poem by Nikolay Gavrilovich
       Poletaev (1889–1935). Poletaev is now all but forgotten.

180   *author of one memoir about Lenin*: Grossman is referring to
       the author Maria Moiseyevna Essen (1872–1956).

188   *law of the Gospel of Christ*: This quote is from a famous
       speech given by Dostoevsky in June 1880, at the unveiling
       of the Pushkin monument in Moscow.

188   *the bridges thunder*: Grossman goes on to refer several times
       to this famous passage from the end of the first part of
       Gogol's *Dead Souls* (translated by Donald Rayfield [London:
       Garnett Press, 2008], 267–8):

       And what Russian does not enjoy riding fast? How can
       his soul, which feels the urge to whirl, to take the bit in
       his mouth, to say sometimes, 'The devil take the hind-
       most,' how can his soul not love riding fast? . . . Oh, the

troika of three horses and a carriage: bird-like troika, who invented you? . . . Russia, are you not also like the bold troika which no-one can overtake? The road is a cloud of smoke under your wheels, the bridges thunder, everything lags behind and is stranded in the rear. The beholder stops, struck by a divine miracle: is this a bolt of lightning from heaven? What does this awe-inspiring movement mean? What sort of unknown force propels these horses which the world has never seen before? Oh, horses, horses, what horses! Does the howling gale have its source in your manes? Is there a keen ear burning on your every sinew? You have caught the sound of a familiar song on high, you have girded your bronze chests together as one and, your hooves barely touching the ground, you have been transformed into just endless lines flying through the air, and the whole troika flies, inspired by God! . . . Russia, where are you hurtling to? Give an answer! There is no answer. The bell peals with a wonderful ringing; the air, ripped to pieces, roars and becomes wind; everything that exists on earth flies past, and other nations and empires look askance and stand back to make way for the troika.

188   *our entire history*: Like the passage Grossman quotes a few lines above, this is from Chaadaev's letter to A. de Sircour of 15 June 1846.

193   *move from one landlord to another*: There are two festivals of St Yury (St George) in the Orthodox calendar, in the spring and in the autumn. Autumn Yury's Day, celebrated on 26 November when the harvest has been completed, had a special importance. A Code of Law introduced in 1497 by Ivan III established the two-week period around Autumn Yury's Day (one week before the feast and one week after it) as the only time of the year when a peasant was free to move from one landowner to another. A century later, Boris Godunov

annulled this freedom, thus finalising the evolution of serfdom.

200 And still more sternly carry on his cause: From 'Lenin', by Sergey Yesenin (1895–1925). 'Lenin' is part of a longer poem, *Gulyay-polye*, written in 1924 (the year of Lenin's death).

200 *'party of a new type'*: Lenin first used this phrase in 1903. He meant by it that the party would be a disciplined, quasi-military organisation – not merely an association of more or less like-minded people.

203 *'Little Apple' and 'The Fried Chicken'*: 'The Fried Chicken' describes how a fried chicken, walking down Nevsky Prospekt, is stopped by the police. Unable to produce his passport or pay a bribe, he is torn to pieces. The last line of the song is 'But chickens want to live too!' 'Little Apple' is another street song from the same period.

204 proletkult: A portmanteau of *proletarskaya kultura* (proletarian culture). This movement, active in the early Soviet Union, aimed to provide the foundation for a truly proletarian art, free from bourgeois influence. Its main theoretician, Aleksandr Bogdanov (1873–1928), saw the *proletkult* as the third part of a revolutionary trinity. While the unions attended to the proletariat's economic interests and the Communist Party to their political interests, the *proletkult* would care for their cultural and spiritual life.

208 *boyars*: The old Russian nobility.

211 *oprichniki*: The unofficial private army of Ivan the Terrible, used to destroy the power of the boyars, or old nobility. The *oprichniki* rode black horses, each with a dog's head and a broom attached to their saddle – a reminder that their duty was 'to bite the enemies of the tsar and sweep away treason'.

215 *gravedigger of freedom*: Grossman is probably alluding to the following passage of *The Communist Manifesto*: 'What the bourgeoisie therefore produces, above all, are its own gravediggers. Its fall and the victory of the proletariat are equally inevitable.'

Chronology

1547–84 Reign of Ivan the Terrible.

1584–1605 Boris Godunov rules Russia. After his death, the country sinks into the period of confusion known as the 'Time of Troubles'.

1703 Peter the Great founds St Petersburg.

1762–96 Reign of Catherine the Great.

1825 Decembrist Revolt: an unsuccessful coup by liberal members of the aristocracy. Tsar Nicholas I comes to the throne.

1842 Publication of Gogol's *Dead Souls*.

1861 Emancipation of the serfs.

1881 Alexander II assassinated by members of the 'People's Will' (Narodnaya Volya) terrorist organisation.

1891 Beginning of construction of Trans-Siberian Railway.

1905 Birth of Vasily Semyonovich Grossman.

1917 Tsar Nicholas II abdicates after February Revolution. Workers' soviets (i.e. councils) are set up in Petrograd and Moscow. Lenin and his Bolshevik Party seize power in the October Revolution.

1918–20 Russian Civil War, accompanied by the draconian economic policies known as 'War Communism'. Although there were many different factions, the two main forces were the Red Army (Communists) and the White Army (anti-Communists). Foreign powers also intervened, to little effect. Millions perished before the Red Army, led by Leon Trotsky, defeated the main White forces in 1920. Less important battles continued until 1923.

1921 After an uprising in March 1921 by sailors at the naval base of Kronstadt, Lenin made a tactical retreat, introducing the at least relatively liberal New Economic Policy (NEP) which lasted until 1928. Many of the more idealistic Communists saw this as a step backwards, as a shameful compromise with the forces of capitalism. The NEP was not, however, accompanied by any political liberalisation.

1924 Death of Lenin. Petrograd is renamed Leningrad. Stalin begins to take over power.

1928–1937 The first and second of Stalin's 'Five-Year Plans' bring about a remarkable increase in the production of coal, iron and steel.

1929 Collectivisation of agriculture begins.

1932–3 Between three to five million peasants die in the Terror Famine in the Ukraine.

1934 Foundation of Union of Soviet Writers. Grossman publishes the story 'In the Town of Berdichev' and a novel, *Glyukauf*, about the lives of the Donbass miners.

1934–9 The great purges. At least a million people are shot and several million sent to the Gulag.

1939 Stalin–Hitler pact. Beginning of Second World War.

1941 Hitler invades the Soviet Union. Leningrad is blockaded and Moscow under threat. Grossman begins to work as a war correspondent for *Krasnaya zvezda* (*Red Star* – the Red Army newspaper).

1945 End of Second World War.

1946 Andrey Zhdanov, then seen as a possible heir to Stalin, tightens control over the arts.

1948 Trofim Lysenko becomes more dominant than ever in Soviet biology, and especially agriculture. Genetics is officially declared a 'bourgeois pseudo-science'. Around 3,000 biologists are fired from their jobs; many are arrested.

1953, 13 January Publication of article in *Pravda* about the Jewish 'Killer Doctors'. Preparations continue for a purge of Soviet Jews. Grossman's recently published novel *For a Just Cause* is fiercely attacked.

5 March Death of Stalin.

4 April Official acknowledgement that the case against the 'Killer Doctors' was entirely false.

1956 Khrushchev denounces Stalin at the Twentieth Party Congress. Millions of prisoners are released from the camps. Start of a more liberal period known as 'The Thaw'.

1958 Publication abroad of *Doctor Zhivago*. Under pressure from the Soviet authorities, Pasternak declines to accept the Nobel Prize.

1961 The KGB confiscates the manuscript of *Life and Fate*.

1962 Publication of Solzhenitsyn's *One Day in the Life of Ivan Denisovich*.

1964 Fall of Khrushchev.

1974 Solzhenitsyn deported after publication in the West of *The Gulag Archipelago*.

1985 Mikhail Gorbachev comes to power. Beginning of the period of liberal reforms known as *perestroika*; the next few years see the first publication in Russia of Grossman's *Life and Fate* and *Everything Flows*, and of important works by Krzhizhanovsky, Platonov, Shalamov, Solzhenitsyn and many others.

1991 Collapse of the Soviet Union.

A Note on Collectivisation and the Terror Famine

These events are so tragic, and so vast, that they can seem entirely beyond understanding. Even Stalin's Great Purges of 1934–8 are easier to understand; they were, among other things, a successful attempt on Stalin's part to destroy, or terrify into submission, any members of the Soviet elite who might conceivably oppose him. It is harder to understand why a ruler should choose to destroy a huge part of the peasantry that had, until then, produced much of the nation's wealth.

What blinds us, perhaps, is the Soviet emblem – the hammer (representing the workers) and the sickle (representing the peasants). The Soviet government referred to itself as a 'workers' and peasants' government' – and we have been too ready to believe them. In actual fact, few of the Bolsheviks ever seem to have had much sympathy with the peasants. Most of them probably felt much the same as Lenin's friend, Maksim Gorky, who once declared, 'You'll pardon my saying so, but the peasant is not yet human . . . He's our enemy, our enemy.' In 1917 Lenin had done his best to buy the support of the peasants with his slogan 'Peace, Bread and Land'; he had encouraged peasants to seize their landlords' estates and burn down their houses. Nevertheless, even then, the peasants had voted not for the Bolsheviks, but for the Social Revolutionaries, whom they rightly saw as more likely to represent their interests. And following 1917, having encouraged the peasants to rise up and seize the land, the Bolsheviks found themselves having to fight a fifteen-year war – with an uneasy truce in the mid-1920s – in order to reassert the power of the central government. The Bolsheviks saw the peasants not only as subhuman but also as wily proto-capitalists whose whole way of life threatened their cherished project of a strong, centrally planned state.

The first measure Stalin took was to destroy the independence of the individual peasants by the imposition of collectivisation; this was carried out throughout the Soviet Union. Stalin's second measure was directed primarily against the Ukraine; the Ukrainian peasants were, for the main part, wealthier and their opposition to collectivisation was particularly strong. The story of the Ukrainian famine is still not widely known, even though Robert Conquest told it over twenty years ago in *The Harvest of Sorrow*. I am grateful to Donald Rayfield for allowing me to include the following pages to provide some general background to Grossman's own painfully vivid account. (Rayfield's article, 'The Ukrainian Famine of 1933: Man-made Catastrophe, Mass Murder, or Genocide?', is included in full in Lubomyr Y. Luciuk, *Holodomor: Reflections on the Great Famine of 1932–1933 in Soviet Ukraine* [Kingston, Canada: Kashtan Press, 2008], 87–93.)

A famine which struck all the grain-producing areas of European Russia, and especially Ukraine, reached a climax in the summer of 1933. It began years earlier, however, when Stalin in the winter of 1929 and 1930 dispossessed, exiled and killed millions of the more prosperous peasants and harassed the remaining peasantry into surrendering land, animals and tools into collective farms; it was made inevitable in the second and final wave of collectivization in the winter of

1930–1931, when a disorganized and disillusioned peasantry was effectively enslaved. This achievement Stalin proclaimed to a congress of peasants in February 1933 to be one 'such as the world has never known before and which no other state in the world has tried to achieve'. At the same time Stalin and his henchmen resolved to industrialize the Soviet Union by selling grain in order to buy machinery from America, Britain and Germany.

By June 1932, as a result of grain confiscation – *khlebzagotovka*, compulsory targets for grain to be delivered to the state – the Ukrainian countryside was already starving. The Secretary of the Ukrainian party, Stanislav Kosior, received letters from young communists, horrified to see, as they put it, 'collective farmers go to the fields and vanish and a few days later the corpse is found and . . . the next day they find the corpse of the man who buried the first one'.

The peasants' attempts to evade grain confiscation or to glean grain from the field were severely punished. The Soviet secret police, OGPU, under the personal supervision of its ailing head, Vyacheslav Menzhinsky, and its ambitious deputy, Genrikh Yagoda, represented in Ukraine by Karl Karlson, monitored the situation and sent squads of men to enforce the containment of the starving peasantry, to punish (or occasionally to condone) cannibalism, and to keep the foreign press away from the countryside. They kept a tally, wherever they could, of deaths, as well as calculating how little food was left in what used to be Europe's breadbasket. Their statistics are one of the foundations for calculating the size of the catastrophe that ensued.

Our sources of information are varied and none are comprehensive or, in themselves, conclusive.

Contemporary sources include letters to relatives abroad (Soviet post offices still accepted such letters until 1935), letters to newspapers (which were then passed on to the secret police), statistics from registry offices, which in most famine-struck areas soon gave up registering deaths. They also include tallies kept for certain months in some areas by OGPU itself, and of course correspondence between party leaders, which was classified until the 1990s. A very few testimonies came from foreign journalists and diplomats, ingenious enough to evade the bans on travel and honest enough to publish stories that were often as unpalatable to their readers in the West as to the Soviet authorities. Later sources for judging the extent of the catastrophe come first from the census figures of 1937, when a deficit of several million in the predicted population of the USSR had to be concealed. In post-Soviet times demographers have been free to look at the age structure of the population and of its mortality in Ukraine before and after the famine, to extrapolate for the Ukrainian countryside as a whole from data for a few areas or a few months the numbers of deaths over the famine period.

For Ukrainian famine areas, the death toll from famine in 1932–1933 appears to depend on the methodology and trustworthiness of the demographer involved. One objective fact is that in 1939 there were 28 million Ukrainians, compared with 31 million in 1926, at a time when (barring famine) the birth rate was often twice the death rate. Deaths are calculated on this basis at anywhere between 2.4 and 4 million. More sophisticated studies give a figure nearer to 5 million. OGPU's tally from December 1932 to mid-April 1933 gives a figure of 2.4 million deaths from famine and cannibalism; by extrapolating these figures for the whole of the famine period, we get a plausible figure of over 7 million deaths. Even the Soviet census figures for 1939 indicate a catastrophe: whereas Ukraine in 1928 had 420,000 deaths and 985,000 births, in 1933 it recorded 1,582,000 deaths and only 34,000 births. Secret figures for the Ukrainian countryside show deaths rising from an acceptable 15,100 in January 1932 to a monstrous 196,200 in June 1932, not stabilizing to 12,000 (in a now much smaller population) until the end of 1934.

Thus, nobody can deny that, in the absence of war or severe droughts, a man-made catastrophe taking the lives of millions of Ukrainian peasants occurred. Because of the absence of full records, because death from starvation is not as easily defined as death from a bullet or in a gas chamber, since it may be disguised as dysentery, typhoid, tuberculosis or suicide, and because it is impossible to say how many more people should have existed in 1934 who didn't, we shall never be able to determine the exact figure, but clearly it is of the same order as the catastrophe that struck Europe's Jews in 1942–1945 or Cambodia's population in 1975–1979.

Mass murder, of course, requires intent, or at the very least the obvious prospect of death as a secondary result of the murderer's actions. The figures for grain production and for grain confiscation in Ukraine, there is no doubt, were fully available to Stalin and Kaganovich, Molotov, Mikoyan, Menzhinsky, Yagoda, the henchmen most responsible for overseeing the Ukrainian famine, and could by simple subtraction only have led them to conclude that millions would die in these areas. Stalin himself deliberately toured the lower Volga area in August 1933, just after the climax of the famine, and saw for himself, without the slightest regret, what he had done. The correspondence of the

Politburo members reveals a full awareness and determination to see the whole process through to the bitter end.

Some of today's neo-Stalinists will admit this, but justify it on the grounds that (a) the grain was needed as the sole means for purchasing modern technology and (b) industrialization was essential to build a Soviet Union strong and well-armed enough to save itself from its enemies. The most cynical neo-Stalinists might add that there was a problem of surplus peasantry in Russia, a problem solved a century earlier by similar famines in countries such as Ireland, or elsewhere, as in Scandinavia, by mass emigration, and that one quick famine was preferable to many more decades of malnutrition. All these arguments are, of course, indefensible: the near defeat of the USSR by Nazi Germany shows that forced industrialization did not save the Soviet Union, so much as the desperation of its people and the help of the Allies. And the state of agriculture in post-Soviet societies is no argument for the murder of so many peasants. Were any of the perpetrators of the famine alive and available for trial, they would therefore have no defence in law against a charge of mass murder.

People, Places and Organisations

Abakumov, Viktor Semyonovich (1908–1954): head of the MGB (formerly known as the NKVD, later as the KGB) from 1946 to 1951. He directed the 1949 purge known as the 'Leningrad Affair'. He was arrested before Stalin's death, 'for lack of zeal in combating the "Doctors' Plot"'. After Stalin's death, he was executed, accused of complicity with Beria, although in fact he and Beria were rivals.

All-Union Central Council of Trade Unions: by far the largest public organisation in the Soviet Union, this served as an umbrella body for the various individual trade unions.

All-Union Society for Cultural Ties with Foreign Countries: the organisation, founded in 1925, that was responsible for all cultural and scientific exchanges and contacts with other countries.

Avvakum (1620–1682): Russian priest who led the opposition to Patriarch Nikon's reform of Russian Orthodox rituals. He was imprisoned, exiled and finally burnt at the stake. His autobiography, written in a vivid, conversational Russian, is an acknowledged masterpiece.

Bakunin, Mikhail Aleksandrovich (1814–1876): along with Prince Kropotkin, the most important Russian anarchist; an opponent of Marx.

Bandera, Stepan Andriyovych (1909–1959): one of the leading figures in the Organisation of Ukrainian Nationalists (OUN), a Ukrainian political movement created in 1929 with the aim of establishing an independent Ukrainian state. The military wing of the OUN, the Ukrainian Insurgent Army, created in 1942, was a major Ukrainian armed resistance movement.

Belinsky, Vissarion Grigoryevich (1811–1848): a leading nineteenth-century Russian literary critic; a radical and a Westerniser.

Benckendorff, Count Aleksandr Khristoforovich (1783–1844): a Russian statesman, now best remembered for having established 'The Third Section', i.e. a secret police force, under Nicholas I, and for having been, in effect, Pushkin's personal censor.

Beria, Lavrenty Pavlovich (1899–1953): head of the NKVD from November 1938 until December 1945; from then until Stalin's death he was deputy prime minister. During the first months after Stalin's death, Beria, Malenkov and Khrushchev formed a ruling 'troika'. In June 1953, however, Beria was arrested; and in December 1953 he was executed.

Bernstein, Eduard (1850–1932): an important German Social Democrat, the founder of the reformist, non-revolutionary current of socialism known as 'evolutionary socialism'.

Black Hundreds: a reactionary, militantly anti-Semitic movement in Russia in the early twentieth century.

Blok, Aleksandr (1880–1921): the finest of the Russian Symbolist poets, referred to by Anna Akhmatova as 'the tragic tenor of the epoch'.

Bolshevik: in 1903, the Russian Social Democrat Party, a Marxist party founded in 1898, split into two factions: the Bolsheviks, led by Lenin, and the Mensheviks, led by Martov. 'Bolshevik' means 'Majority', and 'Menshevik' means 'Minority', but these names are deceptive – the Bolsheviks were, in fact, the smaller faction. They astutely managed to acquire their more impressive name as a result of winning one particular vote, relating to the composition of the editorial board of *Iskra*, the Party's main organ.

Bruno, Giordano (1548–1600): an Italian occult philosopher and cosmologist. Burnt at the stake by the Inquisition, Bruno is sometimes seen as one of the first 'martyrs for science'. He was remarkable both for his intelligence and his courage. In Russian culture, however, his name has become a byword for fanaticism; he has often been contrasted with Galileo, who was, of course, more ready to compromise.

Budyonny, Semyon Mikhailovich (1883–1973): a Civil War hero and ally of Stalin.

Bukharin, Nikolay Ivanovich (1888–1938): one of the most important of the Old Bolsheviks. In 1926 Bukharin became president of the Communist International or Comintern. From 1926 to mid-1928 Bukharin was an ally of Stalin; it was Bukharin who first outlined the Stalinist theory of 'Socialism in One Country'. According to this theory, it was no longer necessary to encourage revolution in the capitalist countries since Russia could and should achieve socialism alone. From mid-1928 Bukharin opposed

Stalin's programme of crash industrialisation and forced collectivisation, supporting a continuation of the more liberal policies (the New Economic Policy, or NEP) that had been in force since 1924. Bukharin was expelled from the Politburo in late 1929; he and his supporters were by then known as the 'Right Opposition' or 'Right Deviationists'. In 1934 Bukharin was 'rehabilitated' by Stalin and appointed editor of *Izvestiya*. Bukharin was arrested in 1937 and charged with conspiring to overthrow the Soviet state. He was tried in March 1938, in the last of the Moscow Show Trials, and executed soon afterwards.

Bulgakov, Sergey Nikolaevich (1871–1944): a Russian Orthodox theologian, philosopher and economist. After a period as a Marxist, he returned to Orthodoxy and, in 1903, published *From Marxism to Idealism.* He published another important book, *Unfading Light*, in 1917, and he was ordained as a priest in 1918. After rising to prominence in Church circles, he was expelled from Russia in late 1922.

Catherine the Great (1729–1796): Empress of Russia from 1762 until 1796. Marrying into the Russian imperial family, she came to power with the deposition of her husband Peter III and presided over a period of growth in Russian influence and culture. During her reign the Russian Empire expanded southward and westward at the expense of both the Ottoman Empire and the Polish-Lithuanian Commonwealth. She wanted to be seen as an enlightened despot and corresponded regularly with Voltaire. At the same time, however, she did more to tie the Russian serf to his land and to his lord than any sovereign since Boris Godunov.

Chaadaev, Pyotr Yakovlevich (1794–1856): an important Russian writer and thinker. His 'Philosophical Letters' are highly critical of Russia's intellectual isolation and social backwardness. Only the first of these 'Letters' was published during his lifetime; the others circulated in manuscript. This first 'Letter' began the long battle, so important in nineteenth-century Russian thought, between the 'Westerners' and the 'Slavophiles'.

Chapaev, Vasily Ivanovich (1887–1919): a Russian Civil War hero. *Chapaev* is the title of a famous 1934 film, based on his exploits. Chapaev is also the subject of countless Soviet jokes.

Chernov, Viktor Mikhailovich (1873–1952): a founder of the Russian Socialist Revolutionary Party. Minister for Agriculture in the Provisional Government in 1917 – and chairman of the Russian Constituent Assembly before it was disbanded by the Bolsheviks in January 1918.

Chernyshevsky, Nikolay Gavrilovich (1828–1889): revolutionary writer and philosopher; the founder of the Populist movement and also major influence on Lenin. In 1862, after being arrested and imprisoned, he wrote the novel *What Is To Be Done?*. This was an important inspiration for Lenin and other Russian revolutionaries. The hero is ascetic and ruthlessly disciplined; in order to develop strength for his work as a revolutionary, he sleeps on a bed of nails and eats only meat.

Chichibabin, Aleksey Yevgenyevich (1871–1945): a chemist who won the Lenin Prize in 1926. After being allowed to go to Paris in 1930, he defected and chose to remain there.

Comintern: the Communist International (also known as the Third International) was an international organisation founded in Moscow in March 1919. Its aim was to fight 'by all available means, including armed force, for the overthrow of the international bourgeoisie and for the creation of an international

Soviet republic as a transition stage to the complete abolition of the State'. The Comintern held seven World Congresses altogether, the last in 1935, but it had lost its importance by the late 1920s. It was officially dissolved in 1943.

Constituent Assembly: a democratically elected constitutional body convened after the October Revolution. It met for thirteen hours on 5–6 January 1918, before being dissolved by the Bolsheviks, who had won only about a quarter of the overall vote. The Bolsheviks had 168 deputies; the Socialist Revolutionaries around twice as many.

Cunow, Heinrich (1862–1936): a German Social Democrat theoretician, critical of Marx.

Degaev, Sergey (1857–1920): an active member of the 'People's Will', and at the same time an agent for the Tsarist Secret Police, or Okhranka. He betrayed several important revolutionaries. He admitted his guilt after being questioned by his comrades and was ordered, under threat of death, to assassinate Colonel Sudeikin, the head of the Okhranka. After assassinating Sudeikin in 1883, he emigrated to the USA and lived the rest of his life there under a false name.

Denikin, Anton Ivanovich (1872–1947): commander of the White armies in the south of Russia during the Civil War.

Eikhe, Robert Indrikovich (1890–1940): Old Bolshevik, responsible for grain requisitioning in the mid-1920s, western Siberia Party chief in the 1930s. Executed in 1940.

Engels, Friedrich (1820–1895): a German social scientist and philosopher, co-author with Karl Marx of *The Communist Manifesto* (1848).

Etinger, Yakov Gilyaryevich (1887–1951): a Jewish doctor accused of killing Zhdanov and Shcherbakov under the pretence of treating them.

Fet, Afanasy Afanasyevich (1820–92): the most important Russian poet of the last quarter of the nineteenth century. The radicals hated him for his conservative political views, but he had a profound influence on the Russian Symbolist movement.

Frankfurt, Semyon Mironovich (1888–1937): in charge of the construction of two of the most important Soviet metalworks, in Kuznetsk and Orsk-Khalilov. Arrested and executed in 1937.

Gershuni, Grigory Andreyevich (1870–1908): one of the founders of the Socialist Revolutionary Party.

Godunov, Boris Fyodorovich (*c*.1551–1605): de facto regent of Russia from 1584 to 1598 and Tsar from 1598 to 1605. After his death, the country sank into the period of confusion known as the 'Time of Troubles'.

Gogol, Nikolay Vasilyevich (1809–1852): a Ukrainian-born Russian writer. The novel *Dead Souls* and the short story 'The Overcoat' (both 1842) are among his masterpieces. Gogol's contemporaries mostly saw him as a social satirist, not realising that Gogol saw himself primarily as a prophet and preacher. Gogol intended *Dead Souls* to be the first part of a modern *Divine Comedy*; the next part was to depict the hero's purification. Gogol, however, ended up burning the second part of the novel in 1852, having come to believe that his imaginative work was sinful. He died soon after this.

Golovaty, Ferapont Petrovich: an old beekeeper from the Volga region who, in December 1942, told local officials that he wanted to give all his personal savings – 100,000 roubles – towards the construction of a warplane for the Stalingrad front. Golovaty's 'personal initiative' received huge publicity.

Gorky, Maksim (1868–1936): a famous writer, seen as a founder of Socialist Realism. Though a friend of Lenin, he criticised him during and after the October Revolution for his suppression of freedom. During the 1920s and early 1930s he lived mainly in Capri. He visited the Soviet Union several times after 1929 and returned for good in 1932, supporting Stalin's cultural policies – though probably with misgivings. He undertook several publishing initiatives, one of which was a series with the general title *The History of Factories and Mills*. The circumstances of his death are obscure; the NKVD chief, Genrikh Yagoda, later confessed to having ordered him to be poisoned by his doctors, but this may have been a false confession. It is, nevertheless, possible that he was killed on Stalin's orders.

Greens: participants in a peasant rebellion in the Tambov Province under the effective leadership of Aleksandr Antonov, a Socialist Revolutionary. At the rebellion's peak in late 1920, the 'Green Army' numbered as many as 50,000.

Gugel, Yakov Semyonovich (1895–1937): in charge of the construction of Magnitogorsk, a vast metalworks in the Urals. Arrested and executed in 1937.

Gvakhariya, Georgy Vissarionovich (1901–1937): the extremely successful director of the S. M. Kirov Iron and Steel Plant in the Donbass region, a huge factory employing some 20,000 workers and hundreds of technical and economic personnel. Arrested and executed in 1937.

Hegel, Georg Wilhelm Friedrich (1770–1831): a German philosopher, one of the founders of German idealism.

Herzen, Aleksandr Ivanovich (1812–1870): an important liberal and pro-Western writer and thinker. From 1857 to 1867, first from London and then from Geneva, he published the radical periodical, *The Bell*. Though banned in Russia, it had a wide illegal circulation there and was of real influence.

Hilferding, Rudolf (1877–1941): an Austrian Social Democrat theoretician, critical of Marx.

Ipatyev, Vladimir Nikolaevich (1867–1952): a prominent Russian chemist. He defected in 1927 and spent the last twenty years of his life in the USA.

Ivan the Terrible (1530–1584): Grand Prince of Moscow from 1533 and 'Tsar of All Russia' from 1547. A devout, intelligent but mentally unstable ruler, whose long reign saw the conquest of the Khanates of Kazan and Astrakhan and transformed Russia into a huge multi-ethnic and multi-confessional state. The first half of his reign saw peaceful reforms and modernisation. In 1565, however, he created the Oprichnina, a section of mainly north-eastern Russia under his own direct rule and policed by his personal servicemen, the *oprichniki*. The Oprichnina was intended as a tool against the powerful hereditary nobility, or boyars, but its creation was an indication of Ivan's increasing paranoia. The second half of his reign was marked by famine, plague, long unsuccessful wars and ever increasing violence on the part of the *oprichniki*.

Izotov, Nikita Alekseyevich (1902–1951): a Donbass miner supposed to have produced, in a single day, over thirty times more coal than the norm.

Kaledin, Aleksey Maksimovich (1861–1918): a Russian cavalry general who led the Don Cossack White armies in the opening stages of the Civil War.

Kalmykov, Betal Edykovich (1893–1940): a Soviet politician from the North Caucasus, First Secretary of the Kabardino-Balkariya autonomous republic.

Kalyaev, Ivan Platonovich (1877–1905): a poet, terrorist and member of the Socialist Revolutionary Party. After assassinating the Grand Duke Sergey Aleksandrovich in 1905, he was hanged.

Kamenev, Lev Borisovich (born Lev Borisovich Rosenfeld, 1883–1936): an important Old Bolshevik. During the period of Lenin's illness (1923–24), Kamenev, Zinoviev and Stalin allied against Trotsky and succeeded in marginalising him. In December 1925, however, Kamenev publicly demanded that Stalin be removed from his position as General Secretary. With only Zinoviev and the Leningrad delegation behind him, Kamenev was defeated. Kamenev then formed a 'United Opposition' with Zinoviev and Trotsky, but this too was crushed; Kamenev, Zinoviev and Trotsky were all expelled from the Party in December 1927. After publicly 'acknowledging their mistakes', both Zinoviev and Kamenev were re-admitted to the Party. They were courted by Bukharin in summer 1928, at the beginning of his own ill-fated struggle with Stalin – but this was reported to Stalin and used against Bukharin. After being arrested in December 1934, Zinoviev and Kamenev were both sentenced to prison. In August 1936, Zinoviev, Kamenev and fourteen others, mostly Old Bolsheviks, were put on trial a second time. The charges included involvement in the assassination of the Old Bolshevik, Sergey Kirov, in 1934, as well as trying to kill Stalin himself. This trial of the 'Trotskyite-Zinovievite Terrorist Centre' was the first of the

Moscow Show Trials. Like the other defendants, Kamenev was found guilty and shot.

Kautsky, Karl (1854–1938): the leading Marxist thinker after the death of his close friend Friedrich Engels and an important figure in the German Social Democratic Party. Lenin considered Kautsky a 'renegade' and Kautsky, for his part, accused Lenin of having laid the foundations for a new dictatorship.

Khataevich, Mendel Markovich (1893–1937): Soviet politician, one of the men responsible for the implementation of the policies that brought about the Terror Famine in the Ukraine. Executed in 1937.

Khodzhaev, Faizulla (1896–1938): prime minister of Uzbekistan from 1925 until 1937. Executed in 1938.

Kibalchich, Nikolay Ivanovich (1853–81): the main explosives expert for the 'People's Will' terrorist organisation; in April 1881 he was hanged for his part in the assassination of Tsar Alexander II. A distant relative of the writer Viktor Kibalchich (better known by his pseudonym of Viktor Serge).

Kirov, Sergey Mironovich (1886–1934): an important Old Bolshevik, who enjoyed considerable popularity. He was assassinated on 1 December 1934. It is probable that Stalin saw him as a rival and ordered this assassination himself. Stalin succeeded, in any case, in using the assassination for his own purposes, as a justification for the Great Purge during which he eliminated the overwhelming majority of the Old Bolsheviks.

Kobulov, Bogdan Zakharovich (1904–1953): a henchman of Beria. Executed after Stalin's death.

Kogan, Mikhail Borisovich (d.1951): one of the 'Killer Doctors', alleged to have worked for many years as an agent of British Intelligence.

Kolchak, Aleksandr Vasilyevich (1874–1920): commander of the White forces in Siberia and the Urals during the Civil War. Executed in 1920.

Komsomol: the Communist Union of Youth, founded in 1918. It played an important role in instilling Communist values in the young, and as an organ for introducing them to the political domain. At its height, in the 1970s, Komsomol membership numbered tens of millions.

Kornilov, Lavr Georgievich (1870–1918): White Army general in southern Russia during the Civil War.

Kropotkin, Prince Pyotr Alekseyevich (1842–1921): the most important Russian anarchist philosopher, and advocate of a communalist society free from central government.

Lavrov, Pyotr Lavrovich (1823–1900): a prominent Russian revolutionary philosopher. He believed that while it would be easy to bring about a *coup d'état* in Russia, the creation of a socialist society needed to involve the masses and – above all – the peasantry.

Left Opposition (or **Left Deviation**): a Communist Party faction opposed to Stalin and led, from 1923 to 1927, by Trotsky.

Lenin, Vladimir Ilyich (born Vladimir Ilyich Ulyanov, 1870–1924): the main leader of the October Revolution and, from 1922, the first leader of the Soviet Union. His father was a successful Russian official in public education. When Lenin was seventeen years old, his eldest brother Alexander was hanged for participating in a plot against the life of Tsar Alexander III. After qualifying as a lawyer and practising for several years, Lenin was arrested in 1895 and sentenced to exile in Siberia, where he associated with Plekhanov and other socialist exiles. In 1900, after his exile came to an end, he left Russia – to spend most of the next seventeen years in Western Europe.

Lenin was an active member of the Russian Social Democrat Party and, in 1903, he led the 'Bolshevik' faction after it split from the 'Menshevik' faction. Until 1917 the Bolshevik Party appeared to be of only marginal importance. Two months after the February Revolution, however, Lenin arrived in Petrograd by train and at once published his *April Theses*, calling for uncompromising opposition to the Provisional Government. Initially, this isolated the Bolsheviks; later, it enabled them to win the support of most of those who were disillusioned with the Provisional Government. After having to flee to Finland in July, Lenin returned to Petrograd in October, inspiring the October Revolution with his slogans of 'Peace, Bread and Land' and 'All Power to the Soviets!'. In January 1918 Lenin shut down the Russian Constitutional Assembly during its first session and formed a coalition government with the left wing of the Socialist Revolutionaries. This coalition soon collapsed, and Lenin outlawed the Socialist Revolutionaries, along with all other political parties.

An attempt on Lenin's life in January 1918 was used to justify a 'Red Terror' against enemies of the Revolution, conducted by the Cheka (the 'Special Committee' or secret police). When Kamenev and Bukharin tried to curb the 'excesses' of the Cheka in late 1918, it was Lenin – consistently an advocate of mass terror – who defended it.

In May 1922, a stroke left Lenin partially paralysed. In December that year and in March 1923, he suffered two more strokes and was left bedridden and unable to speak. After his first stroke, Lenin dictated to his wife a controversial document known as 'Lenin's Testament' – his thoughts about the Party's future leadership. Lenin's wife, Nadezhda Krupskaya, sent this to the Central Committee after Lenin's death, asking for it to be read at the 13th Party Congress in May 1924. Since it included criticisms of all the leading Old Bolsheviks, the Central Committee chose to keep the Testament secret.

Lenin died on 21 January 1924, aged fifty-three. Over 900,000 people passed through the Hall of Columns during the four days and nights that Lenin lay in state. The city of Petrograd was renamed Leningrad in his honour. Within a week of his death, Lenin's body was embalmed and placed on exhibition in the Lenin Mausoleum in Moscow.

Lunacharsky, Anatoly Vasilyevich (1875–1933): as the first Soviet People's Commissar of Enlightenment, he was responsible for Soviet cultural policy and oversaw a huge improvement in Russia's literacy rate. One of the few prominent Old Bolsheviks to die a natural death.

Lysenko, Trofim Denisovich (1898–1976): the dominant figure in Soviet biology, and especially agriculture, from the late 1930s until the mid-1950s. Lysenko was an opponent of Mendelian genetics. His influence peaked in 1948, when genetics was officially declared a 'bourgeois pseudo-science'. All geneticists were fired from their work, and many arrested. Most of Lysenko's scientific claims – for example, his 'discovery' in the late 1940s of strains of wheat that can be grown north of the Arctic Circle – were entirely fraudulent.

MacDonald, James Ramsay (1866–1937): founding figure of the British Labour Party and the first Labour prime minister. His decision in 1931 to form a so-called 'National government', in coalition with the Conservatives, has long been seen by the left as an act of betrayal.

Martov, Julius (real name Yuly Osipovich Zederbaum, 1873–1923): the leader of the Menshevik faction of the Russian Social Democratic Party, a faction that split with the Bolsheviks at the Party Congress held in London in 1903. Once a close friend of Lenin, he was exiled in 1920.

Marx, Karl Heinrich (1818–1883): a revolutionary philosopher and political economist, the father of Communism. Marx argued that capitalism, like previous socio-economic systems, will produce internal tensions which will lead to its destruction. Just as capitalism replaced feudalism, so capitalism will be replaced by communism, though only after a transitional period he referred to as 'the dictatorship of the proletariat'.

Mayakovsky, Vladimir Vladimirovich (1893–1930): poet and playwright, among the most important of the Russian Futurists. A great deal of his work was dedicated to the Bolshevik cause. In April 1930, unhappy in love and disillusioned with Soviet Russia, Mayakovsky shot himself. The words 'Lenin lives, lived and will live' – engraved on monuments all over the Soviet Union – are from his elegy 'Vladimir Ilyich Lenin'.

Mendel, Gregor Johann (1822–1884): an Austrian scientist and Augustinian priest, often called the father of genetics for his study of the inheritance of traits in pea plants. The significance of his work was not recognised until the early twentieth century.

Mendeleyev, Dmitry Ivanovich (1834–1907): a great Russian chemist, the creator of the first version of the periodic table of elements.

Menshevik: in 1903, the Russian Social Democrat Party, a Marxist Party founded in 1898, split into two factions: the Bolsheviks, led by Lenin, and the Mensheviks, led by Martov. Along with all other political parties except for the Bolsheviks, the Mensheviks were banned after the Revolution. In 1921, Lenin wrote, 'The only place for Mensheviks and Socialist Revolutionaries, whether they hide their allegiances or are open about them, is prison.'

Merkulov, Vsevolod Nikolaevich (1895–1953): a henchman of Beria. Arrested and executed at the same time as Beria.

Mikhailov, Timofey Mikhailovich (1859–1881): a member of the 'People's Will', executed for his part in the assassination of Tsar Alexander II.

Mikhailovsky, Nikolay Konstantinovich (1842–1904): a journalist, critic and leading theorist of the Populist movement.

Mikhoels, Solomon Mikhailovich (real name Solomon Mikhailovich Vovsi, 1890–1948): director of the Moscow Yiddish Theatre and chairman of the Jewish Anti-Fascist Committee founded in 1942. In this latter capacity he travelled around the world, encouraging Jewish communities to support the Soviet Union against Nazi Germany. After 1945, however, Stalin opposed contact between Soviet Jews and Jewish communities in other countries and most members of the Jewish Anti-Fascist Committee were arrested. Mikhoels himself was assassinated on orders from Stalin; his death was masked as a car crash.

Nechaev, Sergey Gennadievich (1847–1882): a member of the revolutionary movement known as the Nihilists; he believed in the single-minded pursuit of revolution by any means, including political violence.

Nekrasov, Nikolay Alekseyevich (1821–1878): a Russian radical poet, writer, critic and publisher.

OGPU: over the decades the Soviet State Security Service underwent many changes of name. The most important of these names, in chronological order, are the Cheka (an acronym for 'Special Committee'), the OGPU, the NKVD and the KGB. In post-Soviet Russia the State Security Service is known as the FSB.

Pasternak, Boris Leonidovich (1890–1960): a famous poet. In 1958 he was awarded the Nobel Prize for his novel *Doctor Zhivago*, which was banned in the Soviet Union but had been published in Italy. Under pressure from the authorities, he declined to accept the prize.

People's Will (Narodnaya Volya): a Russian revolutionary organisation, responsible for a number of terrorist attacks including the assassination, in 1881, of Tsar Alexander II. Unlike the Marxists, the People's Will believed that Russia could achieve socialism through a peasant revolution, bypassing the stage of capitalism. Between 1879 and 1883, most of the organisation's members were imprisoned or exiled. At the turn of the century, however, as these veteran revolutionaries were released, they helped to form the Socialist Revolutionary Party. This political party, eventually supported by most of the peasantry, revived many of the goals and methods of the People's Will.

Perovskaya, Sofya Lvovna (1853–1881): a member of the People's Will and wife of Andrei Zhelyabov. She was hanged for her part in the assassination of Tsar Alexander II – the first woman to be executed in Russia for political reasons.

Pestel, Colonel Pavel Ivanovich (1793–1826): one of the chief ideologues of the revolutionary movement known as the Decembrists. Though a democrat in some respects, he believed in a strong, centralised government, with a secret police force to maintain order. He was hanged in July 1826, after the Decembrists' failed coup.

Peter the Great (1672–1725): ruler of Russia, and later the Russian Empire, from 1682 until his death. His policies of Westernisation and expansion transformed Russia into a major European power.

Petlyura, Simon Vasilyevich (1879–1926): the leader of a Ukrainian Nationalist movement that was at its most powerful during 1918 and 1919.

Plekhanov, Georgy Valentinovich (1856–1918): a prominent Socialist philosopher, considered the founder of Russian Marxism.

Postyshev, Pavel Petrovich (1887–1939): a Soviet politician, effectively in charge of the Ukraine during the last stages of the Terror Famine. Arrested in early 1938 and later shot.

Pushkin, Aleksandr Sergeyevich (1799–1837): Russia's greatest poet.

Pyatakov, Georgy Leonidovich (1890–1937): an Old Bolshevik and – after Lenin's death – a member of the 'Left Opposition' to Stalin. In 1936 he was accused of conspiring against the Soviet government with both Trotsky and the Nazis. Executed in January 1937.

Repin, Ilya Yefimovich (1844–1930): the greatest Russian realist painter, a member of the group known as the Peredvizhniki or 'Wanderers'.

Right Opposition (or **Right Deviation**): a Communist Party faction opposed to Stalin in the late 1920s. The most important figures were Bukharin and Rykov. It was this faction that was most closely identified with the New Economic Policy.

Rykov, Aleksey Ivanovich (1881–1938): a prominent Old Bolshevik. Along with Nikolay Bukharin, Rykov led the moderate wing of the Communist Party in the 1920s, promoting a partial restoration of the market economy under NEP. In March 1938, along with Bukharin, Yagoda and others, Rykov was tried at the third Moscow Show Trial, found guilty of treason and executed.

Ryleyev, Kondraty Fyodorovich (1795–1826): a Russian poet and revolutionary, and one of the leaders of the Decembrist revolt.

Ryumin, Mikhail Dmitrievich (1913–1954): as deputy head of the MGB (the Russian Security Service, previously known as the Cheka, the OGPU and the NKVD, later known as the KGB), he took the chief initiative in concocting what became known as the 'Doctors' Plot'. After Stalin's death the case against the doctors unravelled and Ryumin was arrested. He was tried in Moscow and shot in July 1954.

Saltykov-Shchedrin, Mikhail Yevgrafovich (1826–1889): a Russian editor, literary critic and satirical novelist, especially popular in radical circles.

Sazonov, Yegor Sergeyevich (1879–1910): a member of the Socialist Revolutionary Party. In 1904 he assassinated Plehve, the Minister of the Interior. Sentenced to life imprisonment, he poisoned himself in protest against prison conditions.

Scriabin, Aleksandr Nikolaevich (1872–1915): a Russian composer and pianist. His vision of art was close to that of the Russian Symbolist poets.

Semyonov, Nikolay Nikolaevich (1896–1986): a Soviet physical chemist, awarded the Nobel Prize in 1956.

Shcherbakov, Aleksandr Sergeyevich (1901–1945): a Soviet statesman, military leader and politician.

Shchors, Nikolay Aleksandrovich (1895–1919): a talented Ukrainian military commander, renowned for his personal courage during the Russian Civil War. Aleksandr Dovzhenko's film, *Shchors*, was awarded the State Prize of the Soviet Union in 1939.

Shevchenko, Taras Hryhorovych (1814–1861): a Ukrainian poet and artist, the founder of modern Ukrainian literature.

Shostakovich, Dmitry Dmitrievich (1906–1975): the greatest Soviet composer.

Skuratov, Malyuta (d.1573): one of the most brutal henchmen of Ivan the Terrible.

Socialist Revolutionary Party (SRs): founded in 1901–2, this important political party inherited the mantle of the nineteenth-century Populists. Like the earlier People's Will, the Party's left wing, the 'Left SRs', believed in terrorism. The

SRs were the largest party in the Constituent Assembly and enjoyed widespread support among the peasantry.

Stakhanov, Aleksey Grigoryevich (1906–1977): a Soviet miner who was reported, in September 1935, to have mined 227 tons of coal in a single shift. Stakhanov's record set an example throughout the country and gave birth to the Stakhanovite movement; workers who exceeded production targets became known as 'Stakhanovites'.

Stalin, Iosif (born Iosif Vissarionovich Dzhugashvili, 1878–1953): General Secretary of the Communist Party of the Soviet Union's Central Committee from 1922 until his death. During the 1920s and early 1930s he gradually consolidated power until he became a dictator.

Through a series of 'Five-Year Plans' Stalin forced through a programme of rapid industrialisation. His policy of 'Total Collectivisation' (1929–31) led to millions of peasants, derogatorily referred to as 'kulaks', being starved or murdered. In the late 1930s, Stalin launched what has become known as the 'Great Terror'. Like many others, Grossman sees this as having been directed against the Soviet elite and, above all, against the Party elite, the Old Bolsheviks. It does, however, need to be emphasised that members of *any* social or national group which might conceivably have threatened Stalin were deported, sent to the Gulag or executed; over 90 per cent of the nearly 700,000 executions carried out in 1937 and 1938 were of kulaks and members of national minorities.

Stalin's refusal to heed warnings of a German invasion in 1941 led to a series of catastrophic defeats. From 1942, however, the Red Army recovered and, under Stalin's leadership, played a major role in the defeat of Nazi Germany. The Soviet Union went on to become one of just two superpowers in the post-war era.

Sudeikin, Georgy Porfiryevich (1850–1883): head of the Russian Secret Police or 'Third Section'. He ran an important double agent, Sergey Degaev, who eventually assassinated him (see entry on Degaev). It has been suggested that Sudeikin's ultimate aim had been to remove the Tsar and run the country himself, from the Ministry of Internal Affairs.

Timashuk, Lidia Fedoseyevna (1898–1983): one of the physicians attending Andrey Zhdanov during his final illness. Making out that the treatment administered by the heart specialists had been inadequate, she denounced them to the secret police. No attention was paid to her report at the time; after the *Pravda* article about the 'Killer Doctors', however, Lydia Timashuk was awarded the 'Order of Lenin'.

Tolstoy, Aleksey Nikolaevich (1883–1945): an extremely successful Russian writer, nicknamed The Comrade Count, who wrote in many genres but specialised in science fiction and historical novels. In his long historical novel *Peter the First*, he likens Stalin to Peter the Great. As well as being a distant relative of Lev Tolstoy, he is the grandfather of the contemporary writer Tatyana Tolstaya.

Trigoni, Mikhail Nikolaevich (1850–1917): a member of the revolutionary terrorist organisation, the People's Will.

Trotsky, Leon (born Lev Davidovich Bronshtein, 1879–1940): after Lenin, the most important of the leaders of the October Revolution; founder and first commander of the Red Army. After leading the 'Left Opposition' against Stalin, Trotsky was deported from the Soviet Union in 1929. He spent his last years in Mexico, where he was assassinated by one of Stalin's agents in 1940. Of all the Old Bolsheviks, Trotsky was the finest orator and the finest writer.

Vareikis, Iosif Mikhailovich (1894–1939): Old Bolshevik, executed in 1939.

Vinogradova, Yevdokiya Viktorovna (1914–1962): a weaver who, in 1935, set new production records in the textile industry; a female equivalent of Stakhanov.

Virchow, Rudolf (1821–1902): a German doctor and public health activist, known as the 'Father of Pathology'.

Vovsi, Miron Semyonovich (1897–1960): one of the most eminent Soviet doctors, arrested at the time of the 'Doctors' Plot' but released after Stalin's death. First cousin of the actor Solomon Mikhoels.

Vyshinsky, Andrey Yanuaryevich (1883–1954): a lawyer and diplomat, notorious for his vicious speeches as chief prosecutor during the Moscow Trials.

Weissman, Friedrich Leopold August (1834–1914): an important German biologist and evolutionary theorist, opposed to Lamarck's belief in the inheritance of acquired characteristics.

Wrangel, Baron Pyotr Nikolaevich (1878–1928): commander-in-chief of the White Army in the Crimea in the later stages of the Civil War.

Yagoda, Genrikh Grigoryevich (1891–1938): head of the NKVD from 1934 to 1936. Arrested in 1937, tried at the last of the Moscow Trials, in March 1938, and shot soon afterwards.

Yezhov, Nikolay Ivanovich (1895–1940): head of the NKVD during the period of the Great Terror, from September 1936 until November 1938. During this period roughly half of the Soviet political and military establishment was imprisoned or shot. Arrested in 1939, Yezhov was himself shot in 1940.

Yudenich, Nikolay Nikolaevich (1862–1933): a leader of the White forces in north-western Russia during the Civil War.

Zavenyagin, Avraamy Pavlovich (1901–1956): an NKVD colonel general. From 1938 he was in charge of the labour camps of Norilsk. In May 1945 he was appointed head of a team sent to Germany to search for scientists working in the area of nuclear technology.

Zhdanov, Andrey Aleksandrovich (1896–1948): an important Soviet politician, in charge of Soviet cultural policy from 1946 until his death in 1948. He is notorious above all for his attacks on Akhmatova and Zoshchenko in 1946. It is possible that he was killed, on Stalin's orders, by Kremlin doctors.

Zhelyabov, Andrey Ivanovich (1851–1881): a Russian revolutionary and a member of the Executive Committee of the People's Will. One of the organisers of the assassination, on 1 March 1881, of Tsar Alexander II. Although he was arrested, by chance, a few days before the assassination, he demanded that his case be considered together with that of the other conspirators. He was executed along with them.

Zinoviev, Grigory Yevseyevich (1883–1936): a prominent Old Bolshevik. During Lenin's illness, Zinoviev, his close associate Kamenev and Stalin formed a ruling 'troika' in the Communist Party, successfully marginalising Leon Trotsky. In early 1925 the Zinoviev–Kamenev–Stalin 'troika' began to crumble. In late 1925, Stalin, in alliance with Bukharin, succeeded in removing Kamenev and Zinoviev from real power. Zinoviev and Kamenev then formed a 'United Opposition' together with Trotsky. Zinoviev, Kamenev and Trotsky were all expelled from the Communist Party in late 1927. After twice being readmitted to the Party only to be re-expelled, Zinoviev and Kamenev were arrested and sentenced to prison in December 1934. In August 1936, Zinoviev, Kamenev and fourteen others were tried again in the first of the Moscow Show Trials. Zinoviev was executed that month.

Biographical Note

Vasily Semyonovich Grossman was born on 12 December 1905 in Berdichev, a Ukrainian town that was home to one of Europe's largest Jewish communities. In 1934 he published both 'In the Town of Berdichev' – a short story that won the admiration of such diverse writers as Isaak Babel, Maksim Gorky and Boris Pilnyak – and a novel, *Glyukauf,** about the life of the Donbass miners. During the Second World War, Grossman worked as a reporter for the army newspaper *Red Star*, covering nearly all of the most important battles from the defence of Moscow to the fall of Berlin. His vivid yet sober 'The Hell of Treblinka' (late 1944), one of the first articles in any language about a Nazi death camp, was translated and used as testimony in the Nuremberg trials. His novel *For a Just Cause* (originally titled *Stalingrad*) was published in 1952 and then fiercely attacked. A new wave of purges – directed against the Jews – was about to begin; but for Stalin's death, in March 1953, Grossman would almost certainly have been arrested himself. During the next few years Grossman, while enjoying public success, worked on his two masterpieces (neither of which was to be published in Russia until the late 1980s): *Life and Fate* and *Everything*

---

* The title is derived from the German *Glück auf*. This phrase, literally 'Luck up!', was used to greet a miner when he was brought up to the surface. It is used more generally to mean 'Good luck!'.

Flows. The KGB confiscated the manuscript of *Life and Fate* in February 1961. However, Grossman was able to continue working on *Everything Flows*, a novel even more critical of Soviet society than *Life and Fate*, until his last days in hospital. He died on 14 September 1964, on the eve of the twenty-third anniversary of the massacre of the Jews of Berdichev in which his mother had died.

Robert Chandler is the editor of *Russian Short Stories from Pushkin to Buida* and the author of *Alexander Pushkin* (in the Hesperus 'Brief Lives' series). His translations of Sappho and Guillaume Apollinaire are published in the series 'Everyman's Poetry'. His translations from Russian include Vasily Grossman's *Life and Fate* and *The Road*, Leskov's *Lady Macbeth of Mtsensk* and Alexander Pushkin's *The Captain's Daughter*. Together with Olga Meerson and his wife Elizabeth he has translated a number of works by Andrey Platonov. One of these, *Soul*, won the 2004 AATSEEL (American Association of Teachers of Slavonic and East European Languages) prize. His translation of Hamid Ismailov's *The Railway* won the AATSEEL prize for 2007 and received a special commendation from the judges of the 2007 Rossica Translation Prize.

Elizabeth Chandler is a co-translator, with her husband, of Pushkin's *The Captain's Daughter*, of Vasily Grossman's *The Road*, and of several volumes of Andrey Platonov: *The Return, The Portable Platonov, Happy Moscow, Soul* and *The Foundation Pit*.

Anna Aslanyan's translations into Russian include works of fiction by Mavis Gallant, Zadie Smith, Jonathan Lethem, Rod Liddle, and Ali Smith. She is a contributor to the BBC Russian Service.

Yekaterina Korotkova-Grossman, Vasily Grossman's daughter, was born in Kiev. Like her father and grandfather before her, she went to the coal-mining region known as the Donbass, or Donets Basin, after completing her studies. There she worked as an English teacher in a mining village. Later, in Moscow, she worked as a translator of English literature. She has herself written works of fiction set in both historical and contemporary Russia, and she is currently writing a memoir of her years in Tashkent during the Second World War.

Further Reading

Applebaum, Anne, *Gulag: A History of the Soviet Camps* (New York: Doubleday, 2003)

Brent, Jonathan, and Naumov, Vladimir P., *Stalin's Last Crime: The Plot against the Jewish Doctors, 1948–1953* (New York: HarperCollins, 2004)

Conquest, Robert, *The Harvest of Sorrow* (New York: OUP, 1986)

Ellis, Frank, *Vasiliy Grossman* (Oxford: Berg, 1994)

Fitzpatrick, Sheila, *Stalin's Peasants* (New York: OUP, 1996)

Garrard, John and Carol, *The Bones of Berdichev* (New York: The Free Press, 1996)

Graham, Loren R., *Science in Russia and the Soviet Union* (Cambridge: Cambridge University Press, 1993)

Graham, Loren R., *The Ghost of the Executed Engineer* (Cambridge, MA: Harvard University Press, 1996)

Grossman, Vasily, *Life and Fate* (London: Vintage, 2006)

Grossman, Vasily, *A Writer at War*, ed. and trans. Antony Beevor and Luba Vinogradova (London: Pimlico, 2006)

Grossman, Vasily, *The Road* (London: MacLehose Press, 2010)

Kotkin, S., *Magnetic Mountain: Stalinism as a Civilization* (Berkeley: University of California Press, 1997)

Merridale, Catherine, *Night of Stone* (London: Granta, 2001)

Pipes, Richard, *The Degaev Affair: Terror and Treason in Tsarist Russia* (New Haven, CT: Yale University Press, 2003)

Polonsky, Rachel, *A Journey in Russian History* (London: Faber, 2010)

Rayfield, Donald, *Stalin and his Hangmen* (London: Penguin, 2005)

Scott, John, *Behind the Urals* (Bloomington: Indiana University Press, 1989)

Snyder, Timothy, *Bloodlands* (New York: Basic Books, 2010)

Vilensky, Simeon (ed.), *Till my Tale is Told* (London: Virago, 1999)

Viola, Lynne, *The Unknown Gulag* (New York: OUP, 2007)

Acknowledgements

I am grateful to all the following: Denis Akhapkin, Sergey Bunaev, Michael Berry, Marina Brodskaya, Bob Davies, Marya Dmytrieva, John Dunn, David Fel'dman, John and Carol Garrard, Anthony Graybosch, Katia Grigoruk, Anna Gunin, Gasan Gusejnov, Jochen Hellbeck, Alina Israeli, Mikhail Lipyanskiy, Ira Mashinski, Olga Meerson, Tatiana Menaker, Mark Miller, Anna Muza, Katarina Peitlova, Natasha Perova, Joe Roeber, Tim Sergay, Jekaterina Shulga, Peter Stabler, Paul Vaughan, Luba Vinogradova, Sarah Young; to other members of the SEELANGS email group; to my translation students at Queen Mary, University of London; and to Edwin Frank, who edited an earlier version of this translation for NYRB Classics, and Stuart Williams, my editor at Harvill Secker.

We have followed the Russian text as published in *Sobranie sochinenii v 4-kh tomakh* (Moscow: Agraf, 1998). The original manuscript now forms part of the Sakharov Collection in the archives of Harvard University. It was donated by Grossman's biographer John Garrard; he himself received it from Grossman's last love, Yekaterina Vasilievna Zabolotskaya, the prototype of Marya Ivanovna from *Life and Fate*.

I am especially grateful for the generous help of three close relatives of Vasily Grossman. Fyodor Guber (Grossman's stepson) and his daughter Elena Kozhichkina have shown us fascinating photographs and provided me with important factual information. Yekaterina Korotkova-Grossman (Grossman's daughter) has checked the entire translation against the original and saved us from some serious errors. Her afterword follows.

R.C.

Taken in the mid- or late-1950s, this photograph shows Vasily Grossman, sitting, and Nikolay Mikhailovich, Grossman's brother-in-law and the model for Ivan Grigoryevich (© Fyodor Guber)

Afterword

I first heard about this book from a friend, when my father was no longer alive. 'People are talking, you know, about a new short novel by your father. Apparently it's even more uncompromising than *Life and Fate.*' I did not believe my friend. I had never heard of any other book by my father.

All the same, I went round with my husband to Olga Mikhailovna, my father's widow, to ask if she knew what had given rise to these rumours. She immediately took a manuscript from the writing desk and held it out to me. My husband and I read it, though not at one sitting, without leaving Olga Mikhailovna's apartment. I was stunned.

Soon after this, Yekaterina Vasilyevna Zabolotskaya, whom I often visited, showed me the rough drafts. There were a number of them, all with a huge number of corrections and markings in red pencil. The writer had evidently been in an intensely emotional state. The final version was almost twice the length of the first draft. The chapters about Lenin were the last to be written. Stalin at that time was already open to criticism. Lenin, however, still remained on his pedestal.

It was because of these chapters that, in the late 1980s, when *Life and Fate* and the last remaining short stories had already been published, *Everything Flows* was still awaiting its turn. But everyone knew that this would come soon.

The ban had been lifted, and every journal was eager to publish whatever had previously been banned. I had a phone call from Minsk. An animated male voice gaily reeled off a list of requirements: 'Straight from the horse's mouth, the hotter the better – about the camps, about Stalin, about Beria.' I do not like being treated this way, and I replied stonily, 'He didn't write about Beria.'

When it was common knowledge that *Everything Flows* would be published in the journal *October*, the smaller journals all started begging for some small extract. I began negotiating with one that was then very popular.

I have always thought that the two chapters from *Everything Flows* about the famine in the Ukraine are the most powerful in all Grossman's work. Terrible, shocking chapters, written from inspiration. I especially admire the brief second chapter – the unbelievably sad, yet radiant story of the life of a small family. A story about modest people who had led a difficult life, about their self-abnegation, about their great love. I do not know whether Grossman met these people in reality, or whether he imagined them. I know only that he truly loved them. He wrote about this family twice: in the novel *For a Just Cause* and in *Everything Flows*.

To my astonishment, the editor of the popular small journal turned down these chapters. He wanted something about the camps. I refused. This was a time when every newspaper and journal was full of material about the camps, whereas no one had published accounts of the famine. Neither the editor nor I would give in.

At this point someone mentioned *The Family*, saying it was a journal with a huge circulation and that it was very popular with the general reader. This sounded just right – there had, after all, been a long period when the whole country had read and loved my father's work. *The Family* accepted this unexpected present with delight and promptly published it. And, as the editor and I were having a friendly chat about how well everything had turned out, he said, 'There was something irrelevant tacked onto the end. Something about some family – a makeweight. We edited it out.'

A makeweight! How could the editor say this? Why was it that Grossman was so continually unlucky? It took me some time to understand that this kind of thing was only to be expected. Literature can't simply be tailored to suit the fashion of the day. It isn't like an opera libretto that can periodically be 'brought up to date' to amuse the listener.

Sometimes the seed of something bad lies hidden inside something good. The new freedoms of the late 1980s led many editors to choose to publish *only* what had previously been banned. And the blacker, the grimmer, the more shocking, the better . . .

As I said, I had not known of the existence of *Everything Flows*. But I understood in due course that the great queue of former prisoners who came to talk to my father had provided him with material not only for *Life and Fate* but also – and probably to a still greater degree – for *Everything Flows*.

I myself had introduced my father to one of the book's heroes. He was someone I knew well. His name was not Boris Romashkin, but, like Romashkin in *Everything Flows*, he truly had written flyers and posted them on walls. His parents had worked in our trade delegation in England and he had lived there for a long time. The purest and most romantic of Marxists, he had, in due course, returned to Russia. What he found there had shocked him. And he truly had posted flyers . . . One of them, I remember, read, 'Our Red Army does not need officers and epaulettes!' and there were others in a similar vein. He had been arrested at the age of fifteen, and he had spent eleven years in prisons and camps. He was released in the 1950s, but he was never formally 'rehabilitated'.

The document attesting to his release bore the words, 'At the present moment he does not pose any danger.' He worked as a stoker, in the boiler room of some scientific research institute. My father and his friend Semyon Lipkin listened to him for three hours. Every word he said was of interest. There had even been a prisoner who had claimed, in the course of an interrogation, that this famous boy had acted under instructions he had issued himself. It galled him that he, an adult, had been arrested for no reason, whereas this boy – this mere boy – had done something real.

Everything Flows has been published a number of times in Russian, in editions that have been scrupulously prepared. Now it will be read in English, in a fine translation. And my account of how *The Family* edited out the family that Grossman so loved is a mere anecdote, a story about people on the make during a crazy period.

Yekaterina Korotkova-Grossman